State College

at

Framingham

INTRODUCTORY

NUMERICAL ANALYSIS

OF ELLIPTIC BOUNDARY

VALUE PROBLEMS

Harper's Series in Modern Mathematics

I. N. Herstein and Gian-Carlo Rota, Editors

HARPER & ROW, Publishers

New York, Evanston, and London

INTRODUCTORY NUMERICAL ANALYSIS OF ELLIPTIC BOUNDARY VALUE PROBLEMS

DONALD GREENSPAN

Mathematics Research Center, U.S. Army

University of Wisconsin

INTRODUCTORY NUMERICAL ANALYSIS OF ELLIPTIC BOUNDARY VALUE PROBLEMS

Library of Congress Catalog Card Number: 65–11135

6/66

CONTENTS

PREFACE

THERE ARE THREE BASIC REASONS why the time is now propitious for the appearance of specialized, mathematical books on numerical methods. First, successful numerical approaches to nonlinear problems, previously inaccessible by any other method, should be organized and made easily available to applied scientists. Second, mathematical texts are necessary for the growing number of courses in numerical analysis in the various college curricula. And third, in view of the quantity and quality of recent research efforts, the survey book can at best achieve a tone of superficiality. The attempt here is to treat only elliptic boundary value problems by high speed computer, mathematically rigorous numerical techniques.

I thank A. Dou, T. N. E. Greville, S. V. Parter, L. B. Rall, M. Urabe, and M. Yohe for various constructive criticisms of the original manuscript.

DONALD GREENSPAN

INTRODUCTORY

NUMERICAL ANALYSIS

OF ELLIPTIC BOUNDARY

VALUE PROBLEMS

CHAPTER 1

ANALYTICAL PRELIMINARIES

1.1. SETS

One of the basic concepts of modern mathematics is that of a **set**. From a strictly logical point of view, the term *set* may be left undefined. Intuitively, however, a set may be thought of as a collection of objects called elements or points.

The set of no elements is called the **empty set** and will be denoted by $\emptyset$. The empty set plays a role in set theory analogous to the number 0 in the real or complex number system.

The **union**, or **sum**, of two sets A and B, denoted by $A \cup B$, is the set of all elements which belong to at least one of A and B. The union, or sum, of an arbitrary collection of sets A_α, written $\bigcup_\alpha A_\alpha$, is the set of all elements which belong to at least one of the A_α. The **intersection**, or **product**, of two sets A and B, written $A \cap B$, is the set of all elements which belong to both A and B. The intersection of an arbitrary number of sets A_α, written $\bigcap_\alpha A_\alpha$, is the set of all elements which belong to every A_α. $A - B$, or the **difference** of the sets A and B, in that order, is defined to be all those elements of A which are not elements of B.

If every element of a set A is also an element of a set B, one says that A is contained in B, or B contains A, or A is a **subset** of B, and one writes $A \subset B$. Also, it will be convenient to use the notation $x \in A$ to mean x is an element of A and $x \notin A$ to mean x is not an element of A.

1.2. PLANE POINT SETS

Important types of **plane point sets** will be reviewed next. The notions to be considered are fundamental and extend in a natural manner to three, four, and more dimensions. Throughout, the xy plane will be denoted by E^2 and, in general, Euclidean n-space will be denoted by E^n.

In E^2, a **circular neighborhood** of a fixed point $P(\bar{x},\bar{y})$ is the set of all points (x,y) which, for some fixed, positive r, satisfy the relationship $(x - \bar{x})^2 + (y - \bar{y})^2 < r^2$. A convenient notation for a circular neighborhood will be $K(P,r)$. Note that r is always finite and positive and that $(\bar{x},\bar{y})$ is itself an element of $K(P,r)$. The set of points (x,y) whose coordinates satisfy $(x - \bar{x})^2 + (y - \bar{y})^2 \leq r^2$ is called a **circular disc**.

In E^2, a set M is said to be **bounded** iff (i.e., if and only if) there exists a P and an r such that $M \subset K(P,r)$.

In E^2, a point $P(\bar{x},\bar{y})$ is said to be an **interior point** of a set M iff there exists at least one circular neighborhood $K(P,r)$ such that $K(P,r) \subset M$. The **interior** of a set M is defined to be the union of all interior points of M. Furthermore, a set of points M is said to be **open** iff each of its points is an interior point of M.

In E^2, the **complement** of a set of points M is defined to be $E^2 - M$. A set of points M is then said to be **closed** iff $E^2 - M$ is open.

In E^2, a **boundary point** P of a set M is a point for which every circular neighborhood $K(P,r)$ contains at least one point of M and at least one point of $E^2 - M$. Note that P is not necessarily a point of M. The **boundary** of M is defined to be the union of all boundary points of M.

Of particular interest are boundaries which can be given parametrically. Let then a and b be two real numbers with $a < b$. Let $f(t)$ and $g(t)$ be two real-valued, continuous functions for $a \leq t \leq b$ and assume that at least one of $f(t)$ and $g(t)$ is nonconstant on every subinterval $a_1 \leq t \leq b_1$, where $a \leq a_1 < b_1 \leq b$. Then the set of points (x,y) determined by

$$(1.1) \qquad\qquad x = f(t), \quad y = g(t), \qquad a \leq t \leq b$$

is said to be a **bounded plane curve** and equations (1.1) are said to be parametric equations of the curve.

Of course, a bounded plane curve may have a variety of parametric representations.

A bounded plane curve with parametric equations (1.1) is said to be a

closed-curve iff $f(a) = f(b)$ and $g(a) = g(b)$. A bounded plane curve which is a closed-curve is said to be **simple** iff the relationships

$$f(t_1) = f(t_2), \quad g(t_1) = g(t_2), \qquad a < t_1 < b, \quad a < t_2 < b$$

imply $t_1 = t_2$. Furthermore, a bounded plane curve is said to be **sectionally smooth** iff

(a) relative to at least one parametric representation of form (1.1), for each, except possibly a finite number of values of, t in the range $a \le t \le b$, $f(t)$ and $g(t)$ have continuous first and second order derivatives and, at the exceptional points, the corresponding right- and left-hand derivatives exist; and

(b) whenever each exists, neither

$$\left[\left(\frac{df}{dt} \right)^2 + \left(\frac{dg}{dt} \right)^2 \right],$$

nor the corresponding sum of right- or left-hand derivatives is zero.

A **contour**, a type of boundary which will be of particular interest, is defined to be a bounded plane curve which is a simple, sectionally smooth, closed-curve.

We shall have occasion to deal with certain subarcs of contours, defined as follows. If contour S is given by (1.1) and $a < a_1 < b_1 < b$, then the set of points S_1 whose coordinates satisfy $x = f(t), y = g(t), a_1 \le t \le b_1$ is called a closed, proper subarc of S.

By means of the concept of a bounded curve, one can make quite precise, in addition to contour, a useful concept of **connectedness**. In E^2, a set M is said to be **connected** (arcwise) iff for every pair of points P_1, P_2 of M there exists at least one continuous bounded curve C with parametric equations of form (1.1) such that P_1 has coordinates $(f(a),g(a))$, P_2 has coordinates $(f(b),g(b))$, and $C \subset M$.

The concepts of connectedness and that of a bounded plane curve which is a simple, closed-curve are related by the following fundamental theorem.

Theorem 1.1. Jordan Curve Theorem

In E^2, let C be a bounded plane curve which is a simple, closed-curve. Then $E^2 - C$ consists exactly of two open, connected sets A and B, one and only one of which is bounded, such that $A \cap B = \emptyset$ and such that C

is the boundary of both A and B. (For the proof, see Hall and Spencer [1].)

Of the two sets A and B described in Theorem 1.1, the bounded one is called the **inside** of C while the other is called the **outside** of C. In E^2, then, a connected set M is said to be **simply connected** iff, for every bounded plane curve C which is contained in M and which is a simple, closed-curve, the inside of C is also contained in M.

A final type of plane point set that will have varied uses is the **region**, which is defined as any connected, open set different from the empty set.

1.3. LINEAR ELLIPTIC DIFFERENTIAL EQUATIONS

Unless stated otherwise, only *real* numbers and *real* functions will be considered throughout the course of this book. (Only as a reminder, from time to time, will the word *real* be affixed.) The standard notation

$$u_x \equiv \frac{\partial u}{\partial x}, \quad u_y \equiv \frac{\partial u}{\partial y}, \quad u_{xx} \equiv \frac{\partial^2 u}{\partial x^2}, \quad u_{xy} \equiv \frac{\partial^2 u}{\partial x \, \partial y},$$

$$u_{yy} \equiv \frac{\partial^2 u}{\partial y^2}, \quad u_{xxx} \equiv \frac{\partial^3 u}{\partial x^3}, \quad u_{xxy} \equiv \frac{\partial^3 u}{\partial x^2 \, \partial y}, \cdots$$

will be used whenever convenient and if a function u has continuous partial derivatives up to and including order n on a set X, we shall write $u \in C^n(X)$.

Definition 1.1

Let $A = A(x,y)$, $B = B(x,y)$, $C = C(x,y)$, $D = D(x,y)$, $E = E(x,y)$, $F = F(x,y)$ and $G = G(x,y)$ be defined and continuous on a set $R \subset E^2$. At each point of R assume that $A^2 + B^2 + C^2 \neq 0$. Then the linear partial differential equation

$$(1.2) \quad A \frac{\partial^2 u}{\partial x^2} + 2B \frac{\partial^2 u}{\partial x \, \partial y} + C \frac{\partial^2 u}{\partial y^2} + D \frac{\partial u}{\partial x} + E \frac{\partial u}{\partial y} + Fu + G = 0$$

is said to be elliptic at $(x,y) \in R$ iff at that point

$$B^2 - AC < 0.$$

Thus, if $A \equiv 1$, $B \equiv y$, $C \equiv 1 - x^2$, $D \equiv E \equiv F \equiv G \equiv 0$ on E^2, then (1.2) is elliptic at a point (x,y) iff $x^2 + y^2 < 1$, that is, (1.2) is elliptic at each point interior to the unit circle and only at such points.

The prototype elliptic differential equation of mathematical physics is the Laplace, or potential, equation

(1.3)
$$\frac{\partial^2 u}{\partial x^2} + \frac{\partial^2 u}{\partial y^2} = 0,$$

which is elliptic on all of E^2.

Definition 1.2
On a plane point set R, a function $u(x,y) \in C^2(R)$ is said to be harmonic on R iff $u(x,y)$ is a solution of (1.3) at each point of R.

Note, for example, that on any plane region R the functions 1, x, $2y$, $3x - 4y$, $x^2 - y^2$, $x^3 - 3xy^2$ are harmonic.

1.4. THEORETICAL BACKGROUND FOR THE LAPLACE EQUATION

Harmonic functions possess three valuable properties, which will be described next. Let G be a bounded plane point set whose interior R is simply connected and whose boundary S is a contour. If u is harmonic on R and continuous on $G = R \cup S$, then

Property I. u possesses all derivatives of all orders on R (see, e.g., Greenspan [6], p. 120).

Property II. (Strong Max–Min Property) On G, u takes on its maximum and its minimum values on S (see, e.g., Greenspan [6], p. 111).

Property III. (Mean Value Property) If (x_0, y_0) is a point of R and C is any circle in R whose center is (x_0, y_0) and whose radius is r, then (see, e.g., Greenspan [6], p. 122):

(1.4)
$$u(x_0, y_0) = \frac{1}{2\pi r} \int_C u(x,y) \, ds,$$

where the parameter s represents arc length.

Example
Let S be the rectangle whose sides are parallel to the coordinate axes and whose vertices are $(-4,0)$, $(4,0)$, $(4,10)$, $(-4,10)$. Let R be the interior of the rectangle. Consider the function $u = x^2 - y^2$ on $G = R \cup S$. Then

u is continuous on G and harmonic on R. By direct calculation, then, u possesses all derivatives of all orders on R. At the point $(4,0)$ of S, u attains its maximum value on G. Note that u also attains this maximum value at the point $(-4,0)$. Also, at the point $(0,10)$ of S, u attains its minimum value on G. Finally, let C, for example, be the circle of radius one with center at $(2,3)$. Then

$$\frac{1}{2\pi r}\int_C u\, ds = \frac{1}{2\pi}\int_0^{2\pi}[(2+\sin s)^2 - (3+\cos s)^2]\, ds$$

$$= -5$$

$$= u(2,3).$$

Next note that since the Laplace equation has more than one solution on E^2, and hence has more than one solution on any plane point set, one must require additional properties of solutions in order that any resulting problem be well posed, that is, possess a unique solution which depends continuously on supplementary data. In this connection the Dirichlet Problem, the Neumann Problem, and the Mixed Problem have been of interest both theoretically and practically and are described next in detail.

Definition 1.3

In E^2, let G be a bounded point set whose interior R is simply connected and whose boundary S is a contour. If $f(x,y)$ is a given function which is defined and continuous on S, then the **Dirichlet Problem** for the Laplace equation is that of determining a function $u = u(x,y)$ which is

(a) defined and continuous on G,
(b) harmonic on R, and
(c) identical with $f(x,y)$ on S.

Example

The problem of determining a function $u = u(x,y)$ such that

(a) $u(x,y)$ is continuous at each point (x,y) whose coordinates satisfy $x^2 + y^2 \leq 1$;
(b) $u(x,y)$ is harmonic at each point (x,y) whose coordinates satisfy $x^2 + y^2 < 1$;
(c) $u(x,y)$ coincides with $f(x,y) = 1 + x - y$ at each point (x,y) whose coordinates satisfy $x^2 + y^2 = 1$,

is a Dirichlet problem.

The fact that the Dirichlet Problem has a unique solution has been established by a variety of means, including subharmonic and superharmonic functions (Perron [1]), finite differences (Courant, Friedrichs, and Lewy [1]), Green's function (consult Courant and Hilbert [1]), integral equations (consult Lax [1]), Dirichlet's principle (see Courant [1]), and conformal mapping (consult Nehari [1]). The analytical determination of $u(x,y)$, however, is a far more difficult problem than that of establishing its existence. If S is a rectangle, then the solution can be given precisely by Fourier series (Churchill [1], Greenspan [6], Jackson [1]), while if S is a circle, then the solution can be given in terms of the Poisson integral (Courant and Hilbert [1], Greenspan [6], Petrovsky [2]), or Fourier series (John [1]). Also, any problem for which an explicit conformal map can be constructed which takes R onto a rectangular or circular region can be solved in closed form (Nehari [1]). Beyond these cases, the problems involved in constructing u do not seem amenable to existing mathematical techniques.

Definition 1.4

In E^2, let G be a bounded point set whose interior R is simply connected and whose boundary S is a smooth curve with continuously turning tangent. Let $g(x,y)$ be defined and continuous on S. Then the **Neumann Problem** for the Laplace equation is that of finding a function $u(x,y)$ which

(a) is defined and continuous on G,
(b) is harmonic on R, and
(c) has an outwardly directed normal derivative $\dfrac{\partial u}{\partial n}$ which satisfies $\dfrac{\partial u}{\partial n} \equiv g(x,y)$ on S.

It is known that if $\displaystyle\int_S g\,ds = 0$ and if the harmonic function with boundary values $f = \displaystyle\int_0^s g\,ds$ has derivatives of first order which are continuous up to the boundary, that is, which can be defined on the boundary so that the indicated derivatives are continuous on G, then the Neumann Problem has at least one solution (Lax [1], Petrovsky [2]). Moreover, if $u_1(x,y)$ is such a solution, then every solution is of the form $u_1(x,y) + C$, where C is a constant, and, for each constant C, $u_1(x,y) + C$ is a solution (Petrovsky [2]). Thus, under the given assumptions, the Neumann Problem has a one parameter infinity of solutions, and therefore is not well posed. However, the additional assumption that a solution should have a prescribed function value at just one point of S would yield a problem whose solution exists and is unique. Consideration, then, of both normal derivative and function value boundary conditions leads quite naturally to consideration of the following Mixed Problem.

Definition 1.5

In E^2, let G be a bounded point set whose interior R is simply connected and whose boundary S is a smooth curve with continuously turning tangent. For $k \geq 1$, let $S_1, S_2, \cdots, S_k$ be pairwise disjoint, closed, proper subarcs of S and set $S^* = \bigcup_1^k S_i$, $S' = S - S^*$. Let $f(x,y)$ be continuous on S^* and let $g(x,y)$ be bounded and continuous on S'. Then the Mixed Problem for the Laplace equation is that of finding a function $u(x,y)$ which

(a) is defined and continuous on G,
(b) is harmonic on R,
(c) is identical with $f(x,y)$ on S^*, and
(d) has outwardly directed normal derivative $\dfrac{\partial u}{\partial n}$ which satisfies $\dfrac{\partial u}{\partial n} \equiv g(x,y)$ on S'.

Example

The problem of determining a function $u = u(x,y)$ such that

(a) $u(x,y)$ is continuous at each point (x,y) whose coordinates satisfy $x^2 + y^2 \leq 1$,
(b) $u(x,y)$ is harmonic at each point (x,y) whose coordinates satisfy $x^2 + y^2 < 1$,
(c) $u(x,y)$ coincides with $f(x,y) \equiv x^2 - y^2$ at each point (x,y) whose coordinates satisfy both $x^2 + y^2 = 1$, $y \leq 0$, and
(d) the outwardly directed normal derivative $\dfrac{\partial u}{\partial n}$ exists at each point (x,y) whose coordinates satisfy both $x^2 + y^2 = 1$, $y > 0$, and on this set $\dfrac{\partial u}{\partial n} \equiv g(x,y)$, where $g(x,y) = 2x^2 - 2y^2$

is a Mixed Problem.

The fact that certain Mixed Problems have unique solutions appears to have been established first by Lichtenstein [1]. Later efforts are also discussed by Miranda [3], pp. 172–174.

Finally, note that since a simply connected region R and its boundary S are fundamental to the formulation of the Dirichlet, Neumann, and Mixed Problems, we shall reserve these symbols throughout and use them only in the indicated context. Also, it will be assumed throughout that the positive direction of a normal at any point of S', as given in Definition 1.5, is always the outward direction.

EXERCISES

1. Give ten examples of sets.

2. Find $A \cup B$, $A \cap B$ and $A - B$ for each of the following.

(a) A is the set whose elements are the integers 1, 2, and 3; B is the set whose elements are the integers 3, 4, and 5.
(b) A is the set of rational numbers; B is the set of irrational numbers.
(c) A is the set of integers; B is the set of nonnegative integers.
(d) A is the set of real numbers; B is the set of rational numbers.
(e) A is the set of transcendental irrationals; B is the set of algebraic irrationals.

3. Given two sets A and B, prove that $(A \cap B) \subset A$ and $(A \cap B) \subset B$.

4. Given two sets A and B, prove that $A \subset (A \cup B)$ and $B \subset (A \cup B)$.

5. Given the sets A, B, and D, prove that if $A \subset B$ and $B \subset D$, then $A \subset D$.

6. In E^2 describe geometrically each set M, where M is the set of all points (x, y) whose coordinates satisfy:

(a) $x^2 + y^2 < 1$.
(b) $2x^2 + y^2 \geq 4$.
(c) $x^2 + y^2 \geq 0$.
(d) $1 < x^2 + y^2 < 4$.
(e) $1 < x^2 + 2y^2 \leq 9$.
(f) $x + y < 3$.
(g) $x^2 + 2y \geq -1$.

(h) $1 < x < 2, 0 < y < 3$.
(i) $1 < x < 2$, no restriction on y.
(j) $x \geq 0, y \leq 2$.
(k) $|x| < 1, |y| < 2$.
(l) $|x| + |y| > 1$.
(m) $x^2 - y^2 < 1$.

7. If A is the set of points (x, y) in E^2 whose coordinates satisfy $x^2 + y^2 \leq 1$, then find $A \cup M$, $A \cap M$ and $A - M$ for each set M in Exercise 6.

8. For each set M in Exercise 6 determine $E^2 - M$.

9. For each set M of Exercise 6 determine whether or not M is (a) open, (b) closed, (c) bounded, (d) connected, (e) simply connected, (f) a region.

10. Determine the boundary of each set M of Exercise 6.

11. For each of the following give an example of a point set in E^2 which possesses the given properties.

(a) It is open and closed.
(b) It is neither open nor closed.
(c) It is connected but neither open nor closed.
(d) It is closed and not bounded.
(e) It is closed and bounded but not connected.

12. Show that in E^2 any set which consists of a finite number of points is a closed set.

13. Each of the following is a bounded plane curve. Sketch each one and prove that it is a contour.

(a) $x = \cos t,\ y = \sin t,\ 0 \le t \le 2\pi$.
(b) $x = 2 \cos t,\ y = 3 \sin t,\ 0 \le t \le 2\pi$.
(c) On $0 \le t \le 6$

$$x = \begin{cases} t, & 0 \le t \le 1 \\ 1, & 1 \le t \le 3 \\ 4-t, & 3 \le t \le 4 \\ 0, & 4 \le t \le 6 \end{cases}, \qquad y = \begin{cases} 0, & 0 \le t \le 1 \\ t-1, & 1 \le t \le 3 \\ 2, & 3 \le t \le 4 \\ 6-t, & 4 \le t \le 6. \end{cases}$$

(d) On $0 \le t \le 2$

$$x = \begin{cases} \cos t\pi, & 0 \le t \le 1 \\ 2t-3, & 1 \le t \le 2 \end{cases}, \qquad y = \begin{cases} \sin t\pi, & 0 \le t \le 1 \\ 0, & 1 \le t \le 2. \end{cases}$$

(e) On $0 \le t \le 4$

$$x = \begin{cases} t, & 0 \le t \le 2 \\ 2\cos\left(\dfrac{t-2}{2}\right)\pi, & 2 \le t \le 3, \\ 0, & 3 \le t \le 4 \end{cases} \qquad y = \begin{cases} 0, & 0 \le t \le 2 \\ \sin\left(\dfrac{t-2}{2}\right)\pi, & 2 \le t \le 3 \\ 4-t, & 3 \le t \le 4. \end{cases}$$

(f) $x = (2 + \cos t) \cos t,\ y = (2 + \cos t) \sin t,\ 0 \le t \le 2\pi$.

14. For each partial differential equation which follows, determine all those points of E^2 at which the equation is elliptic.

(a) $u_{xx} + u_{yy} + u_y = 0$.
(b) $u_{xx} + u_{yy} + x^2 u_y - 7xy = 0$.
(c) $u_{xx} + u_{yy} + yu_x - xu_y + x^2 u - 3xy = 0$.
(d) $u_{xx} + 2yu_{xy} + (1 - x^2)u_{yy} = 0$.
(e) $u_{xx} + 2yu_{xy} + (1 - x^2)u_y = e^{xy}$.
(f) $u_{xx} - u_{yy} = 0$.
(g) $xu_{xx} + 2yu_{xy} + u_{yy} = 0$.
(h) $yu_{xx} + 2xu_{xy} + 3u_{yy} + 4u_x - yu_y + xyu - e^{xy} = 0$.
(i) $u_{xx} - u_{xy} + (1 + x^2)u_{yy} = u$.

15. For each of the following polynomials in x and y determine numerical values for the coefficients so that the resulting polynomial is harmonic on E^2.

(a) $ax + by$.

(b) $x^2 + bxy + cy^2$.

(c) $ax^3 + bx^2y + cxy^2 + dy^3$.

(d) $x^3 + bx^2y + cxy^2 + dy^3$.

16. Discuss the possibility of finding on E^2, for each fixed $n = 1, 2, 3, \cdots$, a harmonic polynomial of the form

$$\sum_{i=0}^{n} a_i x^i y^{n-i}, \qquad a_0 = 1.$$

17. Let R be the interior of the square S whose vertices are $(0,0)$, $(8,0)$, $(8,8)$, and $(0,8)$. Show that each of the functions $x - y$, $2x^2 - 2y^2$ and $x^3y - y^3x$, defined on $R \cup S$, is harmonic on R, attains its maximum and minimum values on S, and satisfies the Mean Value Property with respect to the circle of radius 2 and center $(3,4)$.

18. Repeat Exercise 17 but for R given as follows.

(a) R is the interior of the triangle S whose vertices are $(0,0)$, $(20,0)$, and $(0,20)$.

(b) R is the interior of the rectangle whose vertices are $(0,0)$, $(10,0)$, $(10,12)$, and $(0,12)$.

(c) R is the interior of the circle S whose center is $(5,4)$ and whose radius is 10.

(d) R is the semicircular region the coordinates of whose points (x,y) satisfy both $x^2 + y^2 < 400$ and $y > 0$.

19. Let R be the region described in Exercise 17. On the four sides of S define $f(x,y)$ by

$$f(x,y) = \begin{cases} 2x^2, & \text{on the side joining } (0,0) \text{ and } (8,0). \\ 128 - 2y^2, & \text{on the side joining } (8,0) \text{ and } (8,8). \\ 2x^2 - 128, & \text{on the side joining } (8,8) \text{ and } (0,8). \\ -2y^2, & \text{on the side joining } (0,8) \text{ and } (0,0). \end{cases}$$

(a) Show that the solution of the associated Dirichlet Problem is $u = 2x^2 - 2y^2$.

(b) Verify that the function defined by

$$u = \begin{cases} 2x^2 - 2y^2, & (x,y) \in S \\ x - y, & (x,y) \in R \end{cases}$$

is not a second solution of the associated Dirichlet Problem.

20. Let R be the region described in Exercise 18(a). On the three sides of S define $f(x,y)$ by

$$f(x,y) = \begin{cases} 0, & (x,y) \text{ on the side joining } (0,0) \text{ and } (20,0). \\ y, & (x,y) \text{ on either of the other two sides.} \end{cases}$$

(a) Show that the solution of the associated Dirichlet Problem is $u(x,y) = y$.

(b) Verify that the function $u = y + xy(2 - x - y)$ is not a second solution of the associated Dirichlet Problem.

21. Let R be the interior of the unit circle $S: x^2 + y^2 = 1$. On S, let $f(x,y) = 1 + x^2 - y$. Show that the solution of the associated Dirichlet Problem is given by

$$u(x,y) = \begin{cases} 1 + x^2 - y, & (x,y) \in S \\ \dfrac{1}{2\pi} \displaystyle\int_{-\pi}^{\pi} \dfrac{(1 + \cos^2 \xi - \sin \xi)(1 - x^2 - y^2)}{1 - 2x \cos \xi - 2y \sin \xi + x^2 + y^2} \, d\xi, & (x,y) \in R. \end{cases}$$

22. Let S be the square with vertices $(0,0)$, $(\pi,0)$, $(0,\pi)$, (π,π), and let R be the interior of S. Define $f(x,y)$ on S as follows.

$$f(x,y) = \begin{cases} 1 - \cos 2x, & (x,y) \text{ on the side joining } (0,0) \text{ and } (\pi,0). \\ 0, & (x,y) \text{ not on the side joining } (0,0) \text{ and } (\pi,0). \end{cases}$$

Show that the solution of the associated Dirichlet Problem is given by

$$u = \sum_{n=1}^{\infty} \left[b_n^* \sin nx \, \frac{\sinh (n\pi - ny)}{\sinh n\pi} \right],$$

where

$$b_1^* = \frac{16}{3\pi}, \quad b_2^* = 0,$$

$$b_k^* = \frac{2}{\pi} \left[\frac{1}{k} - \frac{\cos k\pi}{k} + \frac{\cos (k - 2)\pi}{2(k - 2)} + \frac{\cos (k + 2)\pi}{2(k + 2)} - \frac{1}{2(k - 2)} - \frac{1}{2(k + 2)} \right];$$

$$k = 3, 4, 5, \cdots.$$

23. Let R be the interior of the unit circle S. Assume $g(x,y) \equiv \dfrac{\partial u}{\partial n} = 2x^2 - 2y^2$ on S. Show then that for the associated Neumann Problem there exist an infinite number of solutions of the form $u = x^2 + y^2 + C$, where C is an arbitrary constant.

24. Let R be the interior of the unit circle S. For $(x,y) \in S$ with $y \leq 0$, define $f(x,y) \equiv x^2 - y^2$; while for $(x,y) \in S$ with $y > 0$, define $g(x,y) \equiv \dfrac{\partial u}{\partial n} = 2x^2 - 2y^2$. Show then that the solution of the associated Mixed Problem is $u = x^2 - y^2$.

25. Show that if (r,θ) are polar coordinates of (x,y), then, except at $(0,0)$, the Laplace equation is equivalent to

$$r^2 \frac{\partial^2 u}{\partial r^2} + r \frac{\partial u}{\partial r} + \frac{\partial^2 u}{\partial \theta^2} = 0.$$

CHAPTER 2

THE DIRICHLET PROBLEM FOR THE TWO DIMENSIONAL LAPLACE EQUATION

2.1. INTRODUCTION

Because the Neumann Problem is not well posed, attention will be directed only to Dirichlet and Mixed Problems, and because *in general* solutions of these problems cannot be given in closed form, it becomes reasonable, and indeed often imperative, that methods for approximating solutions be considered. The various methods available for this purpose include finite difference methods (see, e.g., Allen and Robins [1], Batschelet [1], Davidenko [1, 2, 3], Fox [1, 2] Friedrichs [1], Gerschgorin [2], Greenspan [7, 8, 10], Liebmann [1], Mikeladze [1, 2, 3, 4, 5]); variational methods (see, e.g., Collatz [2], Jain [1], Kantorovich and Krylov [1], Krylov and Bogoliubov [1], Lieberstein [2], Myerott, Luke, Clendenin, and Geltman [1], Picone [1, 2], Walsh [1]); method of kernel functions (Bergman [2], Hochstrasser [1], Nehari [2]); Monte Carlo methods (see, e.g., Ehrlich [1]); Newton's method (Bellman, Juncosa, and Kalaba [1]); method of discrete Green's functions (Berger and Lasher [1]); boundary contraction (Chow and Milnes [1, 2, 3], Milnes and Potts [1]); method of the hypercircle (Synge [1]); method of reduction to ordinary differential equations (Albrecht [1], Stresneva [1]); graphical methods (Panov [1], Runge [2]); approximate conformal mapping (see, e.g., Warschawski [1]); and a method of linear programming (J. D. Young [1]).

We shall emphasize in this book the finite difference approach. The Dirichlet Problem will be treated first.

2.2. NUMERICAL PRELIMINARIES

The fundamental approach will be to discretize the Dirichlet Problem by replacing the differential equation by a difference equation and the point set $G = R \cup S$ by a discrete point set $G_h = R_h \cup S_h$. In other words, the given problem, which is one in analysis, will be replaced by an approximate problem, which will be one in algebra. For this purpose consider first developing a difference analogue of Laplace's equation.

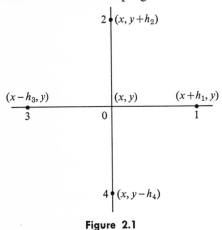

Figure 2.1

Let points (x,y), $(x + h_1, y)$, $(x, y + h_2)$, $(x - h_3, y)$, $(x, y - h_4)$, where h_1, h_2, h_3, h_4 are positive, be numbered 0, 1, 2, 3, 4, respectively, as in Figure 2.1. Let $u(x,y)$ at a point numbered i be denoted by u_i. In a heuristic fashion, let us try to determine parameters α_i, $i = 0$, 1, 2, 3, 4, such that at (x,y)

$$(2.1) \quad u_{xx} + u_{yy} \equiv \sum_{0}^{4} \alpha_i u_i.$$

Since there are five parameters α_i, we seek five relations from which to determine them. Substitution of Taylor expansions about (x, y) for u_1, u_2, u_3, u_4 in (2.1) and regrouping terms implies

$$(2.2) \quad u_{xx} + u_{yy} \equiv u_0(\alpha_0 + \alpha_1 + \alpha_2 + \alpha_3 + \alpha_4) + u_x(h_1\alpha_1 - h_3\alpha_3)$$

$$+ u_y(h_2\alpha_2 - h_4\alpha_4) + \frac{u_{xx}}{2}(h_1^2\alpha_1 + h_3^2\alpha_3)$$

$$+ \frac{u_{yy}}{2}(h_2^2\alpha_2 + h_4^2\alpha_4) + \sum_{1}^{4}[O(\alpha_i h_i^3)],$$

where

$$(2.3) \quad 0 < h_i \leq h, \quad i = 1, 2, 3, 4.$$

If (2.2) were to be a valid identity for *all* functions u, then the corresponding coefficients of u_0, u_x, u_y, u_{xx}, and u_{yy} would be equal. Thus,

(2.4)
$$\left\{\begin{array}{l} \alpha_0 + \alpha_1 + \alpha_2 + \alpha_3 + \alpha_4 = 0 \\ h_1\alpha_1 - h_3\alpha_3 = 0 \\ h_2\alpha_2 - h_4\alpha_4 = 0 \\ h_1^2\alpha_1 + h_3^2\alpha_3 = 2 \cdot \\ h_2^2\alpha_2 + h_4^2\alpha_4 = 2, \end{array}\right.$$

the unique solution of which is

(2.5)
$$\alpha_0 = -2\left[\frac{1}{h_1 h_3} + \frac{1}{h_2 h_4}\right], \quad \alpha_1 = \frac{2}{h_1(h_1 + h_3)}, \quad \alpha_2 = \frac{2}{h_2(h_2 + h_4)},$$

$$\alpha_3 = \frac{2}{h_3(h_1 + h_3)}, \quad \alpha_4 = \frac{2}{h_4(h_2 + h_4)}.$$

Substitution of (2.5) into (2.1) implies then that at (x,y)

(2.6) $\quad u_{xx} + u_{yy} \equiv -2\left[\dfrac{1}{h_1 h_3} + \dfrac{1}{h_2 h_4}\right]u_0 + \dfrac{2}{h_1(h_1 + h_3)}u_1 + \dfrac{2}{h_2(h_2 + h_4)}u_2$

$$+ \frac{2}{h_3(h_1 + h_3)}u_3 + \frac{2}{h_4(h_2 + h_4)}u_4 + \sum_{i=1}^{4}[O(h_i)].$$

Hence, elimination of the terms $\sum_{i=1}^{4}[O(h_i)]$ in (2.6) implies that a difference equation *approximation* of the Laplace equation is

(2.7) $\quad -\left[\dfrac{2}{h_1 h_3} + \dfrac{2}{h_2 h_4}\right]u_0 + \dfrac{2}{h_1(h_1 + h_3)}u_1 + \dfrac{2}{h_2(h_2 + h_4)}u_2$

$$+ \frac{2}{h_3(h_1 + h_3)}u_3 + \frac{2}{h_4(h_2 + h_4)}u_4 = 0.$$

Note that in the particular case $h_1 = h_2 = h_3 = h_4$, (2.7) implies

(2.8)
$$u_0 = \frac{u_1 + u_2 + u_3 + u_4}{4},$$

which is the discrete analogue of the mean value property for harmonic functions. Note also that the numbering 0, 1, 2, 3, 4 is not essential to the form of (2.7). Thus if 0, 1, 2, 3, 4 were replaced, respectively, by 11, 5, 3, 6, 9, then (2.7) need be altered only by replacing u_0, u_1, u_2, u_3, u_4 by u_{11}, u_5, u_3, u_6, u_9, respectively.

Next consider discretizing the given point set $G = R \cup S$. Let $(\bar{x}, \bar{y})$ be an arbitrary point of G and let h be a positive constant. The set of points $(\bar{x} + ph, \bar{y} + qh)$; $p = 0, \pm 1, \pm 2, \cdots$; $q = 0, \pm 1, \pm 2, \cdots$, is called a set of planar grid points. Two such grid points are said to be adjacent iff their distance apart is h. The set of all lines, each of which contains at least one pair of adjacent grid points, is called a planar lattice. Write G_h to designate those points which are either planar grid points in G *or* are points of intersection of S and the planar lattice. If (x,y) is a point of $S \cap G_h$, then (x,y) is called a boundary lattice point, and the set of all boundary lattice points is written S_h. The set of all points of G_h which are not elements of S_h is called the set of interior lattice points and is written R_h. Consideration of G, S, and R will be replaced by consideration of the finite sets G_h, S_h, and R_h, respectively.

R_h is said to be **discretely connected** if every two points of R_h can be connected by a polygonal arc contained in G which consists of straight line segments of constant length h each of whose end points are points of R_h. Throughout this book, R_h is assumed to be discretely connected.

Example

Let R be the bounded region whose boundary S is the triangle with vertices $(0,0)$, $(7,0)$, $(0,7)$. Set $(\bar{x}, \bar{y}) = (0,0)$ and $h = 2$. Then the points of R_h are $(2,2)$, $(2,4)$ and $(4,2)$ and have been crossed in Figure 2.2. The points of S_h are $(0,0)$, $(2,0)$, $(4,0)$, $(6,0)$, $(7,0)$, $(0,2)$, $(5,2)$, $(0,4)$, $(3,4)$, $(0,6)$, $(1,6)$, $(0,7)$ and have been circled in Figure 2.2.

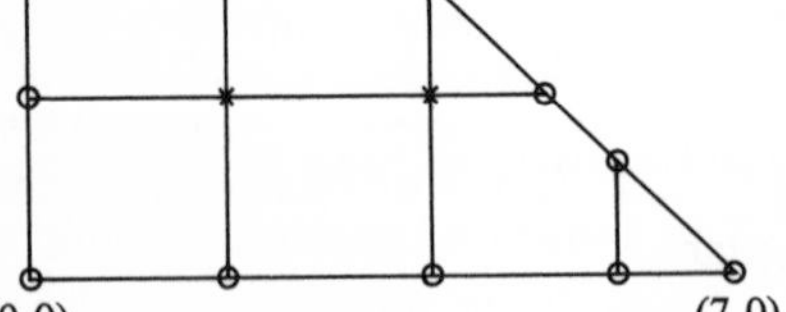

Finally, note that it will be convenient when given a point $(x,y) \in R_h$ to call the four points $(x + h_1, y)$, $(x, y + h_2)$, $(x - h_3, y)$, $(x, y - h_4)$, which are points of G_h and are closest to (x,y) in the east, north, west, and south directions, respectively, the **neighbors** of (x,y), and whenever (x,y) is given as a point of R_h, it will be assumed that the indicated points are its neighbors.

Figure 2.2

2.3. THE NUMERICAL METHOD

The following numerical method will now be given for approximating the unique solution of the Dirichlet Problem. Questions of existence, uniqueness, and convergence will be treated after the method and an example are described.

Method D

Step 1. For fixed $h > 0$ and fixed $(\bar{x},\bar{y})$, construct G_h, R_h, and S_h.

Step 2. Suppose R_h consists of m points, S_h consists of n points, and therefore G_h consists of $m + n$ points. Number the points of R_h in a one-to-one fashion with the integers $1 - m$ in such a way that the numbers are increasing from left to right on any horizontal line of the lattice and increasing from bottom to top on any vertical line of the lattice. Number the points of S_h in a one-to-one fashion with the integers $m + 1$, $m + 2$, $\cdots$, $m + n$.

Step 3. At each point (x,y) of S_h, set $U(x,y) = f(x,y)$. If (x,y) is numbered k, then in subscript notation this is equivalent to $U_k = f(x,y)$.

Step 4. At each point (x,y) of R_h, beginning with the one numbered 1 and continuing in consecutive order through the one numbered m, write down the Laplace difference analogue (2.7) in the form

$$(2.9) \quad -\left(\frac{2}{h_1 h_3} + \frac{2}{h_2 h_4}\right) U(x, y) + \frac{2}{h_1(h_1 + h_3)} U(x + h_1, y)$$

$$+ \frac{2}{h_2(h_2 + h_4)} U(x, y + h_2) + \frac{2}{h_3(h_1 + h_3)} U(x - h_3, y)$$

$$+ \frac{2}{h_4(h_2 + h_4)} U(x, y - h_4) = 0,$$

where $(x + h_1, y)$, $(x, y + h_2)$, $(x - h_3, y)$, $(x, y - h_4)$ are the neighbors of (x,y). If in applying (2.9) at a given point (x,y), any of the points $(x + h_1, y)$, $(x, y + h_2)$, $(x - h_3, y)$, $(x, y - h_4)$ are points of S_h, then in (2.9) replace U at these points by the known values f determined in Step 3. In practice, each equation should be written in subscript notation, as demonstrated in (2.7). There results a linear algebraic system of m equations in the m unknowns $U_1, U_2, \cdots, U_m$.

Step 5. Solve the linear algebraic system generated in Step 4.

Step 6. Let the function U_i, $i = 1, 2, \cdots, m + n$, which is defined only on G_h, represent on G_h the approximate solution of the given Dirichlet Problem.

Example

Let S be the triangle with vertices $(0,0)$, $(7,0)$, $(0,7)$, and let R be the interior of S. On $G = R \cup S$ consider the Dirichlet Problem with $f(x,y) \equiv x^2 - y^2$. Set $(\bar{x},\bar{y}) = (0,0)$ and $h = 2$, as in the previous example. As shown in Figure 2.3 the points of R_h are numbered 1–3 while those of S_h are numbered 4–18. Following the directions of Step 3, one has

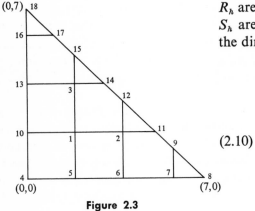

Figure 2.3

$$
\begin{aligned}
U_4 &= 0, & U_{12} &= 7, \\
U_5 &= 4, & U_{13} &= -16, \\
U_6 &= 16, & U_{14} &= -7, \\
U_7 &= 36, & U_{15} &= -21, \\
U_8 &= 49, & U_{16} &= -36 \\
U_9 &= 35, & U_{17} &= -35 \\
U_{10} &= -4, & U_{18} &= -49. \\
U_{11} &= 21,
\end{aligned}
$$

(2.10)

Application next of (2.9) at the point numbered 1 in Figure 2.3 and substitution from (2.10) yields

$$-1U_1 + \tfrac{1}{4}U_2 + \tfrac{1}{4}U_3 + \tfrac{1}{4}(-4) + \tfrac{1}{4}(4) = 0$$

or

(2.11) $$-1U_1 + \tfrac{1}{4}U_2 + \tfrac{1}{4}U_3 = 0.$$

Application of (2.9) at the point numbered 2 in Figure 2.3 and substitution from (2.10) yields

$$-2U_2 + \frac{2}{1(1 + 2)}(21) + \frac{2}{1(1 + 2)}(7) + \frac{2}{2(1 + 2)}U_1 + \frac{2}{2(1 + 2)}(16) = 0$$

or

(2.12) $$\tfrac{1}{3}U_1 - 2U_2 = -24.$$

Application of (2.9) at the point numbered 3 in Figure 2.3 and substitution from (2.10) yields

$$-2U_3 + \frac{2}{1(1+2)}(-7) + \frac{2}{1(1+2)}(-21)$$

$$+ \frac{2}{2(1+2)}(-16) + \frac{2}{2(1+2)}U_1 = 0$$

or

(2.13)
$$\tfrac{1}{3}U_1 - 2U_3 = 24.$$

The solution of (2.11)–(2.13) is

(2.14)
$$U_1 = 0, \quad U_2 = 12, \quad U_3 = -12.$$

Thus, U_i, $i = 1, 2, \cdots, 18$, as given by (2.10) and (2.14), constitutes the approximate solution to the given Dirichlet Problem on the discrete set G_h.

Note that in previously described finite difference techniques (see, e.g., Batschelet [1], Gerschgorin [2], Greenspan [3]), the grid boundary points S_h need not have been points of S, whereas in Method D they are. The present definition of S_h is used because practical experience has indicated that when S_h need not be a subset of S, the maximum numerical error over G_h has occurred on S_h and numerous examples have consistently indicated that the application of Method D yields improved accuracy.

Observe that Method D prescribes an ordering to the system of algebraic equations generated in Step 4, that is, there is a first equation, a second equation, $\cdots$, an mth equation. The significance of the ordering is that in the ith equation, $i = 1, 2, \cdots, m$, the coefficient of x_i is, in absolute value, the maximum coefficient in the equation. In terms of matrices, one would say that the matrix of the coefficients has a dominant diagonal, and such dominance is of great value in discussing the solution of large linear algebraic systems by iteration (see, e.g., Varga [1]).

Note also that actually $m = m(h)$ and $n = n(h)$. Throughout, however, we shall consistently write merely m for the number of points of R_h and n for the number of points of S_h.

The reasonableness of Method D will be established next by showing that the approximate solution always exists and is unique and that for a large class of problems the approximate solution converges to the analytical solution as h goes to zero.

2.4. UNIQUENESS OF THE APPROXIMATE SOLUTION

It will be of value now and in later considerations to establish the following two algebraic lemmas.

Lemma 2.1

Suppose, for fixed integral $k \geq 1$,

(2.15)
$$\alpha_0 < 0,$$

(2.16)
$$\alpha_i > 0, \qquad i = 1, 2, \cdots, k,$$

(2.17)
$$\sum_0^k \alpha_i \leq 0,$$

(2.18)
$$\sum_0^k \alpha_i \beta_i \geq 0.$$

If

(2.19)
$$\beta_0 > 0$$

and

(2.20)
$$\beta_0 \geq \beta_i, \qquad i = 1, 2, \cdots, k,$$

then

(2.21)
$$\beta_0 = \beta_i, \qquad i = 1, 2, \cdots, k,$$

while if

(2.22)
$$\beta_0 < 0$$

and

(2.23)
$$\beta_0 \leq \beta_i, \qquad i = 1, 2, \cdots, k,$$

then

(2.24)
$$\beta_0 = \beta_i, \qquad i = 1, 2, \cdots, k.$$

Proof:

First, in addition to (2.19) and (2.20), assume that

(2.25)
$$\beta_0 > \beta_1.$$

Then

(2.26)
$$\beta_i = \beta_0 - r_i, \qquad i = 1, 2, \cdots, k,$$

where $r_1 > 0$ and $r_i \geq 0$, $i = 2, 3, \cdots, k$. Substitution of (2.26) into (2.18) implies

$$(2.27) \qquad 0 = \sum_0^k \alpha_i \beta_i = \alpha_0 \beta_0 + \sum_1^k \alpha_i \beta_i = \alpha_0 \beta_0 + \sum_1^k \alpha_i (\beta_0 - r_i)$$

$$= \beta_0 \sum_0^k \alpha_i - \sum_1^k \alpha_i r_i.$$

Hence, from (2.17),

$$(2.28) \qquad 0 \leq -\sum_1^k \alpha_i r_i.$$

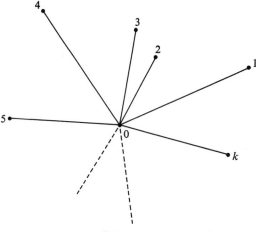

Figure 2.4

However, from (2.16) and the definition of r_i, $i = 1, 2, \cdots, k$, it follows that

$$(2.29) \qquad 0 > -\sum_1^k \alpha_i r_i,$$

and a contradiction has been reached. Thus (2.25) is not possible and by (2.20) it follows that $\beta_0 = \beta_1$. In an analogous fashion, it follows that $\beta_0 = \beta_i$, $i = 1, 2, \cdots, k$, which establishes (2.21). In a similar fashion (2.22) and (2.23) imply (2.24) and the lemma is proved.

The next lemma, also of great value, is stronger than, yet similar to, Lemma 2.1. If one considers a star of points numbered 0, 1, $\cdots$, k, as in Figure 2.4, and if one knows that u_0 is in some sense an average of

$u_1, u_2, \cdots, u_k$, then it will be necessary to have conditions under which $u_0 = u_1 = \cdots = u_k$. The following result will be of importance in this connection.

Lemma 2.2. (*Star Lemma*)

Suppose $\alpha_0 < 0$; $\alpha_i > 0$, $i = 1, 2, \cdots, k$; $\sum_0^k \alpha_i = 0$, and $\sum_0^k \alpha_i \beta_i = 0$.

Then

$$\beta_0 \geq \beta_i, \qquad i = 1, 2, \cdots, k$$

implies

$$\beta_0 = \beta_1 = \cdots = \beta_k,$$

while

$$\beta_0 \leq \beta_i, \qquad i = 1, 2, \cdots, k,$$

also implies

$$\beta_0 = \beta_1 = \cdots = \beta_k.$$

Proof:
The proof follows in the same fashion as that of Lemma 2.1.

Theorem 2.1. (*Strong Max–Min Property*)
For fixed R_h and S_h let U_j, $j = 1, 2, \cdots, m + n$, be any function defined on $R_h \cup S_h$ which satisfies (2.9) at each point of R_h. Then U_j attains both its maximum value M and its minimum value m on S_h.

Proof:
Suppose U_j attains its maximum value M at some point (x,y) of R_h. Then since Lemma 2.2 is applicable to (2.9), it follows that

$$(2.30) \qquad M = U(x,y) = U(x + h_1, y).$$

If $(x + h_1, y)$ is a point of S_h, the theorem is proved. If $(x + h_1, y)$ is not a point of S_h, then one can repeat the argument to show that the values of U at the four neighbors of $(x + h_1, y)$ are also equal to M. Thus, since $R_h \cup S_h$ contains only a finite number of points, it follows that in a finite number of steps one can show that $U(x^*,y^*) = M$, where $(x^*,y^*) \in S_h$. By a completely analogous argument, U_j also attains its minimum value on S_h, and the theorem is proved.

Corollary. (*Weak Max–Min Property*)

For fixed R_h and S_h, let U_j, $j = 1, 2, \cdots, m + n$, be any function defined on $R_h \cup S_h$ which satisfies (2.9) at each point of R_h. Then

$$(2.31) \qquad \min_k [0, U_k] \le U_j \le \max_k [0, U_k], \qquad \begin{array}{l} j = 1, 2, \cdots, m + n \\ k = m + 1, m + 2, \cdots, m + n \end{array}$$

and, in particular,

$$(2.32) \quad \max_j |U_j| \le \max_k |U_k|, \qquad \begin{array}{l} j = 1, 2, \cdots, m + n \\ k = m + 1, m + 2, \cdots, m + n. \end{array}$$

Proof:

The proof follows directly from Theorem 2.1.

Note that the Weak Max–Min Property (2.31) can be established even if (2.9) were replaced by a difference equation whose coefficients satisfied the assumptions of Lemma 2.1. As this result will be fundamental later to the consideration of elliptic equations other than the Laplace equation, it will be formulated now as a lemma.

Lemma 2.3. (*Weak Max–Min Property*)

Let U_j, $j = 1, 2, \cdots, m + n$, be defined on $R_h \cup S_h$ and satisfy at each point of R_h a difference equation of the form $\sum\limits_0^4 \alpha_i U_i = 0$, where the α_i satisfy the conditions of Lemma 2.1. Then (2.31) and hence (2.32) are valid.

Proof:

Suppose $U > 0$ at some point of R_h. Then, since R_h is finite, there is some point, numbered say 0, of R_h, at which U is maximal on R_h. Thus, $U_0 > 0$ and $U_0 \ge U_i$, $i = 1, 2, 3, 4$. Then, by Lemma 2.1, $U_0 = U_i$, $i = 1, 2, 3, 4$. In a finite number of steps, then, U must assume the value U_0 at a point of S_h. Similarly, if $U < 0$ at some point of R_h, then U must assume its least negative value at some point of S_h. Thus (2.31) and hence (2.32) are valid and the proof is complete.

Note that the method of Theorem 2.1 and Lemma 2.3 by which one starts at a point of R_h and proceeds in a step-by-step fashion to a point of S_h is called a **march to the boundary technique**.

Theorem 2.2

For fixed h and fixed $(\bar{x}, \bar{y})$, the numerical solution described in Method D exists and is unique.

Proof:

In order to prove the theorem, it will suffice to show that the linear algebraic system generated by Step 4 of Method D has a unique solution. To do this, it will suffice to show that if $f(x,y) \equiv 0$, the resulting homogeneous system has only the zero solution. However, the zero vector is a solution of this system and, by (2.32), it is the only solution. Thus the theorem is proved.

With regard to Theorem 2.2, note that even though the numerical solution possesses a strong max–min property, only the weak max–min property is utilized in the proof. Later, this observation coupled with Lemma 2.3 will permit the extension of almost the entire present discussion to elliptic equations other than Laplace's equation.

It will be of value to explore next the structure of various matrices associated with Method D.

Definition 2.1

For fixed $(\bar{x}, \bar{y})$, fixed h, and any function V_j, $j = 1, 2, \cdots, m + n$, defined on G_h, the linear operator $\mathscr{D}_h^{(1)}$ is defined at each point $(x,y) \in R_h$ by

$$(2.33) \quad \mathscr{D}_h^{(1)}[V(x,y)] = -2\left(\frac{1}{h_1 h_3} + \frac{1}{h_2 h_4}\right)V(x,y) + \frac{2}{h_1(h_1 + h_3)}V(x + h_1, y)$$

$$+ \frac{2}{h_2(h_2 + h_4)}V(x, y + h_2) + \frac{2}{h_3(h_1 + h_3)}V(x - h_3, y)$$

$$+ \frac{2}{h_4(h_2 + h_4)}V(x, y - h_4),$$

where $(x + h_1, y)$, $(x, y + h_2)$, $(x - h_3, y)$, $(x, y - h_4)$ are the four neighbors of (x,y).

A convention followed with respect to (2.33) is that if V is defined on R, and V^* is the restriction of V to R_h, then we will write $\mathscr{D}_h^{(1)}[V(x,y)]$ for $\mathscr{D}_h^{(1)}[V^*(x,y)]$. Also, for simplicity, we shall often write $\mathscr{D}_h^{(1)}[V]$ or $\mathscr{D}_h^{(1)}V$ for $\mathscr{D}_h^{(1)}[V(x,y)]$.

Theorem 2.3

Given $(\bar{x}, \bar{y})$ and h for Method D, there exists a unique $m \times m$ "Green's matrix" $B = B(h) = (b_{ij}(h)) = (b_{ij})$ and a unique $m \times n$ "Green's boundary matrix" $\dot{B} = \dot{B}(h) = (\dot{b}_{ij}(h)) = (\dot{b}_{ij})$, such that for any V_k, $k = 1, 2, \cdots, m, m + 1, \cdots, m + n$, defined on G_h, one has on R_h

$$(2.34) \qquad V_i = \sum_{j=1}^{m} [b_{ij}\mathscr{D}_h^{(1)} V_j] + \sum_{j=1}^{n} [\dot{b}_{ij}V_{m+j}], \qquad i = 1, 2, \cdots, m.$$

Moreover, B is nonsingular and

$$(2.35) \qquad \dot{b}_{ij} \geq 0, \qquad i = 1, 2, \cdots, m; \quad j = 1, 2, \cdots, n.$$

$$(2.36) \qquad \max_i \sum_{j=1}^{n} |\dot{b}_{ij}| = 1, \qquad i = 1, 2, \cdots, m.$$

$$(2.37) \qquad b_{ij} \leq 0, \qquad i = 1, 2, \cdots, m; \quad j = 1, 2, \cdots, m.$$

Proof:

Write the linear algebraic system of Method D in the form

$$(2.38) \qquad \sum_{s=1}^{m} a_{is}U_s = \sum_{j=1}^{n} \dot{a}_{ij}U_{j+m}, \qquad i = 1, 2, \cdots, m.$$

By Theorem 2.2, (2.38) can be written in the equivalent form

$$(2.39) \qquad U_i = \sum_{k=1}^{n} \dot{b}_{ik}U_{m+k}, \qquad i = 1, 2, \cdots, m,$$

where

$$(2.40) \qquad \dot{b}_{ik} = \sum_{l=1}^{m} b_{il}\dot{a}_{lk}, \qquad i = 1, 2, \cdots, m; \quad k = 1, 2, \cdots, n$$

and

$$(2.41) \qquad (b_{ij}) = (a_{ij})^{-1}, \qquad i, j = 1, 2, \cdots, m.$$

If one is given now V_k, $k = 1, 2, \cdots, m, m + 1, \cdots, m + n$ on G_h, then at each point of R_h let

$$(2.42) \qquad \mathscr{D}_h^{(1)} [V_i] = k_i, \qquad i = 1, 2, \cdots, m,$$

which is equivalent to

$$(2.43) \qquad \sum_{s=1}^{m} a_{is}V_s = k_i + \sum_{j=1}^{n} \dot{a}_{ij}V_{j+m}, \qquad i = 1, 2, \cdots, m,$$

where the a_{is} and $\dot{a}_{is}$ are given by (2.38). Then, as above, (2.43) implies

$$(2.44) \qquad V_i = \sum_{s=1}^{m} b_{is}k_s + \sum_{j=1}^{n} \dot{b}_{ij}V_{j+m}, \qquad i = 1, 2, \cdots, m,$$

where the b_{is} and b_{ij} are given by (2.40) and (2.41). But, from (2.42), it follows that (2.44) has the equivalent form

$$(2.45) \qquad V_i = \sum_{s=1}^{m} b_{is} \mathscr{D}_h^{(1)}[V_s] + \sum_{j=1}^{n} \dot{b}_{ij} V_{j+m}, \qquad i = 1, 2, \cdots, m,$$

from which the first part of the theorem readily follows.

In order to establish (2.35)–(2.37), assume first for each $l = 1, 2, \cdots, n$, that $V_j^{(l)}, j = 1, 2, \cdots, m + n$, is the solution of (2.42) with $k_i = 0$, $i = 1, 2, \cdots, m$, and $V_{r+m} = \delta_{rl}$, $r = 1, 2, \cdots, n$, where δ_{rl} is the Kroneker delta. From (2.44) then, $V_i^{(l)} = \dot{b}_{il}$. From (2.31), $0 \leq V_i^{(l)} \leq 1$, $i = 1, 2, \cdots, m$, so that $\dot{b}_{ij} \geq 0$ for $i = 1, 2, \cdots, m$, $j = 1, 2, \cdots, n$. Next let $V_i, i = 1, 2, \cdots, m, m + 1, \cdots, m + n$, be the solution of (2.42) for which $k_i = 0, i = 1, 2, \cdots, m, V_i = 1, j = m + 1, \cdots, m + n$. Then, from (2.44),

$$V_i = \sum_{j=1}^{n} \dot{b}_{ij} = \sum_{j=1}^{n} |\dot{b}_{ij}|.$$

But, by Theorem 2.1, $V_i = 1$ for $i = 1, 2, \cdots, m$, so that

$$\max_i \sum_{j=1}^{n} |\dot{b}_{ij}| = 1, \qquad i = 1, 2, \cdots, m.$$

Finally, let $V_i^{(l)}$ be the solution of (2.42) with $k_i = \delta_{il}$ and $V_j = 0, j = m + 1, \cdots, m + n$. Then, by (2.44), $V_i^{(l)} = b_{il}$. But $\mathscr{D}_h^{(1)}[V_i^{(l)}] \geq 0$ on R_h and $V_{m+1}^{(l)} = V_{m+2}^{(l)} = \cdots = V_{m+n}^{(l)} = 0$ imply by Lemma 2.1 that $V_i^{(l)}$ cannot be positive on R_h. Hence, (2.37) is valid and the theorem is proved.

Example

In order to clarify some of the content of Theorem 2.3, consider the following example. Let S be the hexagon with consecutive vertices $(1,0)$, $(2,0), (3,1), (2,2), (1,2)$ and $(0,1)$ and let R be the interior of S (see Figure 2.5). For $(\bar{x}, \bar{y}) = (0,0)$ and $h = 1$, number the points $(1,1)$ and $(2,1)$, of R_h, 1 and 2, respectively. Number the points of S_h with $3, 4, \cdots, 8$, as indicated in Figure 2.5. The equations

$$\mathscr{D}_h^{(1)}[U_i] = 0, \qquad i = 1, 2$$

are

$$-4U_1 + U_2 = \qquad\qquad - U_5 - U_6 - U_7$$
$$U_1 - 4U_2 = - U_3 - U_4 \qquad\qquad\qquad - U_8.$$

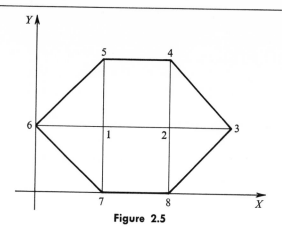

Figure 2.5

Hence,

$$(a_{ij}) = \begin{pmatrix} -4 & 1 \\ 1 & -4 \end{pmatrix}, \quad (\dot{a}_{ij}) = \begin{pmatrix} 0 & 0 & -1 & -1 & -1 & 0 \\ -1 & -1 & 0 & 0 & 0 & -1 \end{pmatrix}.$$

B then is given by

$$(b_{ij}) = (a_{ij})^{-1} = \begin{pmatrix} -\tfrac{4}{15} & -\tfrac{1}{15} \\ -\tfrac{1}{15} & -\tfrac{4}{15} \end{pmatrix}$$

and

$$(\dot{b}_{ij}) = (b_{ij})(\dot{a}_{ij}) = \begin{pmatrix} \tfrac{1}{15} & \tfrac{1}{15} & \tfrac{4}{15} & \tfrac{4}{15} & \tfrac{4}{15} & \tfrac{1}{15} \\ \tfrac{4}{15} & \tfrac{4}{15} & \tfrac{1}{15} & \tfrac{1}{15} & \tfrac{1}{15} & \tfrac{4}{15} \end{pmatrix}.$$

2.5. CONVERGENCE

Let the linear operator $\mathscr{L}$ (for Laplace) be defined for all functions v which have continuous second partial derivatives on R by

(2.46) $$\mathscr{L}[v] = v_{xx} + v_{yy}.$$

Lemma 2.4

Let $v(x,y) \in C^2(G)$. Then at any point $(x,y) \in R_h$

(2.47) $$\mathscr{D}_h^{(1)}[v(x,y)] = \mathscr{L}[v(x,y)] + \Omega[v(x,y)],$$

where

(2.48) $$\Omega[v(x,y)] = \frac{h_1}{h_1 + h_3} v_{xx}(\xi_1, y) + \frac{h_2}{h_2 + h_4} v_{yy}(x, \xi_2)$$

$$+ \frac{h_3}{h_1 + h_3} v_{xx}(\xi_3, y) + \frac{h_4}{h_2 + h_4} v_{yy}(x, \xi_4) - v_{xx}(x,y) - v_{yy}(x,y),$$

and

(2.49)

$$x < \xi_1 < x + h_1, \; y < \xi_2 < y + h_2, \; x - h_3 < \xi_3 < x, \; y - h_4 < \xi_4 < y.$$

Proof:

The proof is a direct result of substitution of finite Taylor expansions into (2.47).

Now let B and $\dot{B}$ be the matrices described in Theorem 2.3. The **row norms** $\|B\|$ and $\|\dot{B}\|$ are defined by

$$(2.50) \qquad \|B\| = \max_i \left\{ \sum_{j=1}^{m} |b_{ij}|, \quad i = 1, 2, \cdots, m \right\}$$

$$(2.51) \qquad \|\dot{B}\| = \max_i \left\{ \sum_{j=1}^{n} |\dot{b}_{ij}|, \quad i = 1, 2, \cdots, m \right\}.$$

Theorem 2.4

Let B and $\dot{B}$ be the matrices described in Theorem 2.3. Then, independently of h,

$$(2.52) \qquad \|\dot{B}\| = 1$$

and there exists a constant a such that

$$(2.53) \qquad \|B\| \leq \frac{a^2}{8}.$$

Proof:

From Definition 2.1 and equation (2.36), (2.52) follows immediately. Next without loss of generality, assume that for each $(x,y) \in G$, $x \geq 0$, $y \geq 0$. Then since G is bounded, there exists a positive constant a such that $0 \leq x \leq a$ for all $(x,y) \in G$. Let G^* be the infinite strip which consists of all (x,y) whose coordinates satisfy $0 \leq x \leq a$, $-\infty < y < \infty$ and let R^* be the interior of G^*. Then the function

$$(2.54) \qquad w(x,y) = \tfrac{1}{8}(2x - a)^2$$

has the properties

$$(2.55) \qquad \Omega[w] = 0, \qquad \text{on } G^*$$

$$(2.56) \qquad 0 \leq w \leq \frac{a^2}{8}, \qquad \text{on } G^*$$

$$(2.57) \qquad \mathscr{L}[w] = 1, \qquad \text{on } R^*.$$

Moreover, from (2.47), (2.55), and (2.57) it follows that at each point of R_h,

$$(2.58) \qquad \mathscr{D}_h^{(1)}[w] = 1,$$

so that (2.34) implies

$$(2.59) \qquad w(x,y) = \sum_{j=1}^{m} b_{ij} + \sum_{j=1}^{n} [\dot{b}_{ij} w_{n+j}], \qquad i = 1, 2, \cdots, m.$$

Since $w \geq 0$, (2.59) yields

$$\sum_{j=1}^{m} [-b_{ij}] \leq \sum_{j=1}^{n} [\dot{b}_{ij} w_{n+j}], \qquad i = 1, 2, \cdots, m$$

from which it follows from (2.35)–(2.37), (2.52), and (2.56) that

$$\sum_{j=1}^{m} |b_{ij}| \leq \sum_{j=1}^{n} [|\dot{b}_{ij}| (w_{n+j})], \qquad i = 1, 2, \cdots, m.$$

$$\leq \| \dot{B} \| \cdot \sup w$$

$$\leq \frac{a^2}{8} .$$

Hence, from (2.50)

$$\| B \| \leq \frac{a^2}{8}$$

and the theorem is proved.

Lemma 2.5

Let $u(x,y)$ be the unique solution of the Dirichlet Problem and let $U_k,\ k = 1, 2, \cdots, m, m + 1, \cdots, m + n$, be the approximate solution generated by Method D. Let $B, \dot{B}$ be those matrices described in Theorem 2.3. Then if $u \in C^2(G)$ it follows that on R_h

$$(2.60) \qquad U_i - u_i = - \sum_{j=1}^{m} (b_{ij}\Omega[u_j]), \qquad i = 1, 2, \cdots, m.$$

Proof:

In (2.34), set $V(x,y) = U(x,y) - u(x,y)$, so that

$$U_i - u_i = \sum_{j=1}^{m} [b_{ij}\mathscr{D}_h^{(1)}(U_j - u_j)] + \sum_{j=1}^{n} [\dot{b}_{ij}(U_{m+j} - u_{m+j})]$$

$$= - \sum_{j=1}^{m} [b_{ij}\mathscr{D}_h^{(1)}(u_j)].$$

But, $\mathscr{L}[u] = 0$, so that by (2.47)

$$U_i - u_i = - \sum_{j=1}^{m} [b_{ij}\Omega(u_j)], \quad i = 1, 2, \cdots, m,$$

which proves the lemma.

Definition 2.2

Let u be the analytical solution of the Dirichlet Problem, and for fixed h and fixed $(\bar{x},\bar{y})$ let $U_j,\ j = 1, 2, \cdots, m, m + 1, \cdots, m + n$, be the numerical solution generated by Method D. Let X be a subset of G_h. Then the error $E(X)$ is defined by

$$(2.61) \qquad E(X) = \max_{(x,y)\in X} |U(x,y) - u(x,y)|.$$

Of course, by construction, $E(S_h) = 0$, so that

$$(2.62) \qquad E(G_h) = E(R_h).$$

We shall now show that for a large class of Dirichlet problems the numerical solution generated by Method D converges to the analytical solution as h converges to zero.

Theorem 2.5

For fixed $(\bar{x},\bar{y})$, it follows with regard to Definition 2.2 that if $u \in C^2(G)$ then

$$(2.63) \qquad \lim_{h\to 0} E(G_h) = 0.$$

Proof:

By (2.60), (2.61), and (2.62), one has

$$E(G_h) = E(R_h)$$

$$\le \|B\| \, [\max_j |\Omega(u_j)|, \qquad j = 1, 2, \cdots, m]$$

$$\le \frac{a^2}{8} \, [\max_j |\Omega(u_j)|, \qquad j = 1, 2, \cdots, m]$$

$$= \frac{a^2}{8} \bigg[\max \bigg| \frac{h_1}{h_1 + h_3} u_{xx}(\xi_1, y) + \frac{h_2}{h_2 + h_4} u_{yy}(x, \xi_2)$$

$$+ \frac{h_3}{h_1 + h_3} u_{xx}(\xi_3, y) + \frac{h_4}{h_2 + h_4} u_{yy}(x, \xi_4) - u_{xx} - u_{yy} \bigg| \bigg]$$

$$\le \frac{a^2}{8} \bigg[\max \bigg\{ \frac{h_1}{h_1 + h_3} |u_{xx}(\xi_1, y) - u_{xx}(x,y)|$$

$$+ \frac{h_2}{h_2 + h_4} |u_{yy}(x, \xi_2) - u_{yy}(x,y)| + \frac{h_3}{h_1 + h_3} |u_{xx}(\xi_3, y) - u_{xx}(x,y)|$$

$$+ \frac{h_4}{h_2 + h_4} |u_{yy}(x, \xi_4) - u_{yy}(x,y)| \bigg\} \bigg]$$

$$\le \frac{a_2}{8} \, [\max \{ |u_{xx}(\xi_1, y) - u_{xx}(x,y)|$$

$$+ |u_{yy}(x, \xi_2) - u_{yy}(x,y)| + |u_{xx}(\xi_3, y) - u_{xx}(x,y)|$$

$$+ |u_{yy}(x, \xi_4) - u_{yy}(x,y)| \}].$$

Now, since $u \in C^2(G)$, u_{xx} and u_{yy} are uniformly continuous on G. Thus, given $\epsilon > 0$ there exists $\delta(\epsilon)$ such that $(x_1 - x_2)^2 + (y_1 - y_2)^2 < \delta$ implies $|u_{xx}(x_1,y_1) - u_{xx}(x_2,y_2)| < \epsilon$ and $|u_{yy}(x_1,y_1) - u_{yy}(x_2,y_2)| < \epsilon$. Thus, given $\epsilon > 0$, for all sufficiently small h,

$$E(G_h) \le \frac{a^2}{2}\,\epsilon,$$

from which (2.63) and the theorem follow readily.

It is of interest to note that Theorem 2.5 states that convergence is **pointwise** and the proof shows convergence to be **uniform**.

2.6. COMPUTATIONAL CONSIDERATIONS

Though Theorem 2.5 assures convergence for solutions $u \in C^2(G)$, it does not provide a computable error bound for $E(R_h)$. Thus, from the practical point of view, one knows from it only that $U_i \to u_i$ on R_h as $h \to 0$ and the selection of h must be determined completely by the capacity of the digital computer available. However, for very recent results concerning computable error bounds for special types of regions consult J. Nitsche and J. C. C. Nitsche [1]. It is also of interest to note that for certain nonfinite difference methods of approximation computable error bounds have been given (Bramble and Payne [1], Fichera [2, 3, 4], Lieberstein [2]); these are not pointwise, however, but are bounds in some L_p sense. Furthermore, with regard to the condition $u \in C^2(G)$ in Theorem 2.5, often one need only require $u \in C^2(R)$. However, the only available written material at present in this direction can be found in John [2].

With regard to selecting a numerical method for solving the algebraic system for Method D, some sort of iteration always seems to be preferable. A modification of Newton's method called successive over-relaxation (consult the Appendix) has proved to be of particular practical value. For rectangular domains one can determine after an appropriate grid selection the over-relaxation factor ω which yields the maximum rate of convergence (Frankel [1]). For nonrectangular regions, however, one cannot usually calculate ω, even though when symmetry is present it can be given explicitly by formula (see equation (A.21)), and methods for approximating it are still being investigated (Garabedian [1], Parter [2], D. Young [2]).

TABLE 2.1

x	y	Approximate Solution U by Method D	Exact Solution $u = -x^3 - 3x^2y + 3xy^2 + y^3$
.01	.01	.00000000	.00000000
.02	.40	.07311199	.07311200
.04	.85	.69668095	.69668100
.05	.65	.33299997	.33300000
.06	.05	−.00018100	−.00018100
.08	.30	.04232799	.04232800
.09	.99	1.21013966	1.21011400
.10	.73	.52598694	.52598700
.12	.25	.02559700	.02559700
.13	.52	.21750296	.21750300
.15	.80	.74262490	.74262500
.17	.13	−.00536800	−.00536800
.18	.98	1.35871972	1.35872000
.20	.70	.54499991	.54500000
.22	.56	.29063194	.29063200
.24	.19	−.01380500	−.01380500
.26	.40	.09010397	.09010400
.28	.70	.56800790	.56800800
.32	.20	−.04780798	−.04780800
.33	.69	.53848791	.53848800
.36	.83	.94643886	.94644390
.37	.51	.16125196	.16125200
.39	.05	−.07908399	−.07908400
.41	.39	−.01919600	−.01919600
.43	.65	.37958793	.37958800
.44	.89	1.14844481	1.14844500
.47	.11	−.15832797	−.15832800
.52	.72	.45727993	.45728000
.55	.55	.00000000	.00000000
.58	.81	.66049092	.66049100
.59	.24	−.34023493	−.34023500
.63	.40	−.35992693	−.35992700
.64	.70	.16149598	.16149600
.67	.01	−.31402800	−.31402800
.71	.30	−.59290090	−.59290100
.75	.65	−.29350000	−.29350000
.79	.10	−.65556893	−.65556900
.80	.56	−.65894391	−.65894400
.83	.17	−.84625188	−.84625200
.86	.37	−1.05315684	−1.05315700
.93	.02	−.85512696	−.85512700
.99	.14	−1.32098500	−1.32098500

For problems in which the choice of grid size h and the memory capacity of the computer preclude the application of Method D, one should consult the modification of Rosser [1].

Finally, from the variety of examples run on the CDC 1604, the following is presented in order to show typical results obtainable by Method D.

Let G be the set of points (x,y) which satisfy the conditions $x^2 + y^2 \leq 1$, $x \geq 0$, $y \geq 0$, so that G has the shape of a quarter circle. Then the points of R satisfy the conditions $x^2 + y^2 < 1$, $x > 0$, $y > 0$. Consider the Dirichlet Problem on G with $f = -x^3 - 3x^2y + 3xy^2 + y^3$ on S. Set $h = .01$ and $(\bar{x}, \bar{y}) = (0,0)$. Then, of course, the approximate solution contains no error on S_h. R_h contains 7750 points and the resulting 7750 equations determined by application of (2.9) were resolved by successive over-relaxation with $\omega = 1.8$ and zero initial vector. The running time was 37 minutes and selected, but typical, results are recorded in Table 2.1. For specific programming techniques, consult Greenspan and Yohe [1].

EXERCISES

1. Let S be the triangle with vertices $(0,0)$, $(7,0)$ and $(0,7)$, and let R be the interior of S. On $G = R \cup S$ consider the Dirichlet Problem with $f(x,y) = x - y$.

(a) By Method D find the approximate solution on R_h for each of the following.
  (i) $(\bar{x}, \bar{y}) = (0,0)$, $h = 1$. (iv) $(\bar{x}, \bar{y}) = (0,0)$, $h = .05$.
  (ii) $(\bar{x}, \bar{y}) = (0,0)$, $h = .5$. (v) $(\bar{x}, \bar{y}) = (0,0)$, $h = .01$.
  (iii) $(\bar{x}, \bar{y}) = (0,0)$, $h = .25$. (vi) $(\bar{x}, \bar{y}) = (.5,0)$, $h = 2$.
(b) Since $u = x - y$ is the exact solution of the given Dirichlet Problem, calculate $E(R_h)$ for each case of part (a).

2. Let S be the ellipse given by $25x^2 + 9y^2 = 225$ and let R be the interior of S. On $G = R \cup S$ consider the Dirichlet Problem with $f(x,y) = x^2 - y^2$.

(a) By Method D find the approximate solution on R_h for each of the following.
  (i) $(\bar{x}, \bar{y}) = (0,0)$, $h = 1$. (iii) $(\bar{x}, \bar{y}) = (0,0)$, $h = .25$.
  (ii) $(\bar{x}, \bar{y}) = (0,0)$, $h = .5$. (iv) $(\bar{x}, \bar{y}) = (0,0)$, $h = .1$.
(b) Since $u = x^2 - y^2$ is the exact solution of the given Dirichlet Problem, calculate $E(R_h)$ for each case of part (a).

3. Let R be the region which consists of all points (x,y) which satisfy $x^2 + y^2 < 4$, $x > 0$, $y > 0$. Let S be the boundary of R. On $G = R \cup S$ consider the Dirichlet Problem with $f(x,y) = x^3 y - y^3 x$.

(a) By Method D find the approximate solution on R_h for each of the following.

    (i) $(\bar{x},\bar{y}) = (0,0)$, $h = 1$.   (iii) $(\bar{x},\bar{y}) = (0,0)$, $h = .25$.

    (ii) $(\bar{x},\bar{y}) = (0,0)$, $h = .5$.   (iv) $(\bar{x},\bar{y}) = (0,0)$, $h = .1$.

(b) Since $u = x^3 y - y^3 x$ is the exact solution of the given Dirichlet Problem, calculate $E(R_h)$ for each case of part (a).

4. Let U_i, $i = 1, 2, \cdots, m + n$, be the numerical solution obtained by applying Method D to a Dirichlet Problem. Show that if $M = \max U_i$ on G_h and $U_i = M$ at some point of R_h, then $U_i = M$, $i = 1, 2, \cdots, m + n$, i.e., U_i is constant on G_h.

5. Is Lemma 2.1 still valid if (2.19) is replaced by $\beta_0 \geq 0$ and (2.22) is replaced by $\beta_0 \leq 0$?

6. For each of the following functions calculate $\mathscr{D}_h^{(1)}$ as defined in (2.33).

(a) $V(x,y) = 1$.   (e) $V(x,y) = 3x^2 - 2xy + y^2$.

(b) $V(x,y) = 2y$.   (f) $V(x,y) = y^5$.

(c) $V(x,y) = x - 5y$.   (g) $V(x,y) = e^y \sin x$.

(d) $V(x,y) = x^2 - 2y$.

7. For the R, S, R_h, and S_h displayed in Figure 2.3, determine the elements of the matrices B and $\dot{B}$ of Theorem 2.3. Also, calculate $\|B\|$ and $\|\dot{B}\|$ directly from the matrices.

8. Generalize Method D by introducing a "rectangular" rather than a "square" grid, i.e., instead of constructing the grid with the points $(\bar{x} + ph, \bar{y} + qh)$, $p = 0, \pm 1, \pm 2, \cdots, q = 0, \pm 1, \pm 2, \cdots$, construct one with the points $(\bar{x} + ph_1, \bar{y} + qh_2)$, $p = 0, \pm 1, \pm 2, \cdots, q = 0, \pm 1, \pm 2, \cdots, h_1 > 0$, $h_2 > 0$.

9. Let R be a bounded, simply connected region whose boundary S is a circle. Let $f(x,y)$ be continuous on S. The Exterior Dirichlet Problem is that of finding a function $u(x,y)$ such that

    (a) $u_{xx} + u_{yy} \equiv 0$ on $E^2 - (R \cup S)$,

    (b) $u \in C(E^2 - R)$,

    (c) $u \equiv f$ on S.

It is known that the Exterior Dirichlet Problem has a unique solution (Petrovsky [2]). Devise a method for approximating this unique solution by first applying an inversion to the given problem. Discuss the assets and liabilities of your method.

10. (a) If one utilizes only the weak, not the strong, max–min property in the proof of Theorem 2.3, show that one could not establish (2.36), but could prove

$$(2.36') \qquad \max_i \sum_{j=1}^n |b_{ij}| \le 1, \qquad i = 1, 2, \cdots, m.$$

(b) Show that Theorem 2.5 still is valid if (2.36) is replaced by (2.36').

CHAPTER 3

THE MIXED PROBLEM FOR THE TWO DIMENSIONAL LAPLACE EQUATION

3.1. INTRODUCTION

With regard to the Mixed Problem (see Definition 1.5 and the related discussion), the new ingredient which must be considered is the outwardly directed, normal derivative $\dfrac{\partial u}{\partial n}$, referred to hereafter only as the **normal**. For the purpose of approximating $\dfrac{\partial u}{\partial n}$, fix h, let $(\bar{x},\bar{y}) \in S^*$, and construct G_h, R_h, and S_h as for the Dirichlet Problem. R_h is of course assumed to be discretely connected. Set $S_h = S_h^* \cup S_h'$ where S_h^* consists of those points of S_h that are also points of S^*, and S_h' consists of those points of S_h that are also points of S'. For *simplicity*, it will be assumed in this chapter that each point of S_h^* is a neighbor of some point of R_h. (This latter assumption, though not severely restrictive, *can be avoided* by the introduction of the concept of an effective boundary as in Motzkin and Wasow [1], or by what Warten [1] has called the $D_{k,h}$-boundary.) Furthermore, if the axis of the normal at $(x,y) \in S'$ is defined as the straight line through (x,y) which is orthogonal to S at (x,y), then it will be assumed throughout that the axis of each given normal intersects in at least two points that part of the planar lattice which is contained in G.

3.2. TECHNIQUES FOR APPROXIMATING NORMAL DERIVATIVES

Two methods for approximating normal derivatives will now be explored.

Technique I

Approximations of first order follow readily by means of linear interpolation. Three cases are considered.

Case A. Suppose that at $(x,y) \in S_h'$, and numbered 0 (see Figure 3.1a), the axis of the normal is directed inward and first meets the lattice in a

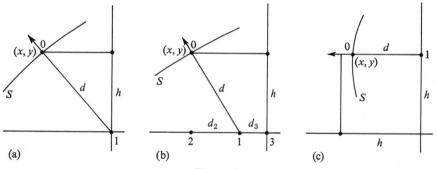

Figure 3.1

point of R_h which has been numbered 1. Then

$$(3.1) \qquad \frac{(u_0 - u_1)}{d} \equiv \frac{\partial u}{\partial n}\bigg|_0 + 0(d),$$

so that, as an approximation, we have

$$(3.2) \qquad \frac{(u_0 - u_1)}{d} = \frac{\partial u}{\partial n}\bigg|_0.$$

Case B. Suppose that at $(x,y) \in S_h'$, and numbered 0 (see Figure 3.1b), the axis of the normal is directed inward and first meets the lattice in a point numbered 1 that is not a point of G_h. Then this point lies in the interior of a closed segment of the lattice which contains exactly two points, numbered 2 and 3, of G_h and of which, we assume, at least one is a point of R_h. Let the positive distances between 0 and 1, 1 and 2, and 1 and 3 be d, d_2, and d_3, respectively. Then linear interpolation for u_1 in terms of

u_2 and u_3 and substitution into (3.1) readily yields the approximation

(3.3) $$\frac{u_0}{d} - \frac{d_2}{d(d_2 + d_3)} u_3 - \frac{d_3}{d(d_2 + d_3)} u_2 = \left.\frac{\partial u}{\partial n}\right|_0.$$

Case C. Suppose that at $(x,y) \in S_h'$, and numbered 0 (see Figure 3.1c), the normal is parallel to a line of the lattice. Suppose then that the associated axis is directed inward and meets a first lattice point that is a point of R_h and is numbered 1. If the distance between 0 and 1 is d, where, of course, $0 < d \le h$, then set

(3.4) $$\frac{(u_0 - u_1)}{d} = \left.\frac{\partial u}{\partial n}\right|_0.$$

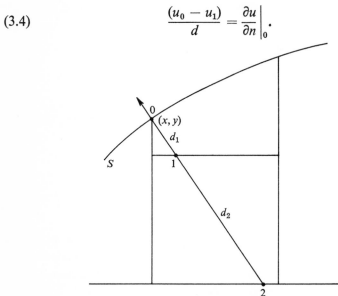

Figure 3.2

Consider next the construction of *second* order approximations. This can be accomplished in a variety of ways. For example, using the arrangement shown in Figure 3.2, one could first consider the second order approximation (Milne [1], p. 96)

(3.5) $$\frac{2d_1 + d_2}{d_1(d_1 + d_2)} u_0 - \frac{d_1 + d_2}{d_1 d_2} u_1 + \frac{d_1}{d_2(d_1 + d_2)} u_2 = \left.\frac{\partial u}{\partial n}\right|_0$$

and then use quadratic interpolation to express u_1 and u_2 in terms of u at other points of G_h, provided of course that these points exist. We shall examine however in greater detail a second method for which more experimental support is available.

Technique II

The applicability of the following method is, of course, limited to domains for which point patterns of the indicated type do exist. Two cases will be considered.

Case A. Suppose that at $(x,y) \in S'_h$, and numbered 0 (see Figure 3.3), the normal is parallel to a line of the lattice. Assume then that the associated axis is directed inward; that it meets, in consecutive order, the points

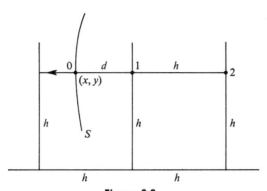

Figure 3.3

1 and 2 of G_h; that there are no points of G_h between 0 and 2 except 1; and that the line segment which has 0 and 2 for end points is contained in G. Let the distance between 0 and 1 be d and that between 1 and 2 be h. Then, as in (3.5), a second order approximation is given by

$$(3.6) \qquad \frac{h + 2d}{d(h + d)} u_0 - \frac{h + d}{hd} u_1 + \frac{d}{h(h + d)} u_2 = \frac{\partial u}{\partial n}\bigg|_0 .$$

Case B. Suppose that at $(x,y) \in S'_h$, and numbered 0, the normal is not parallel to a line of the lattice. It will be assumed then that at each such point one can find an arrangement of points of G_h which has one of the eight patterns shown in Figure 3.4, where $0 < d \le h,\ 0 < e \le h$.

Consider first the arrangement in Figure 3.4a. Let α be the angle, measured counterclockwise, from the positive x-axis to the normal at (x,y), $0 \le \alpha < 2\pi$. Then

$$\frac{\partial u}{\partial n}\bigg|_0 \equiv \frac{\partial u}{\partial x}\bigg|_0 \cos \alpha + \frac{\partial u}{\partial y}\bigg|_0 \sin \alpha .$$

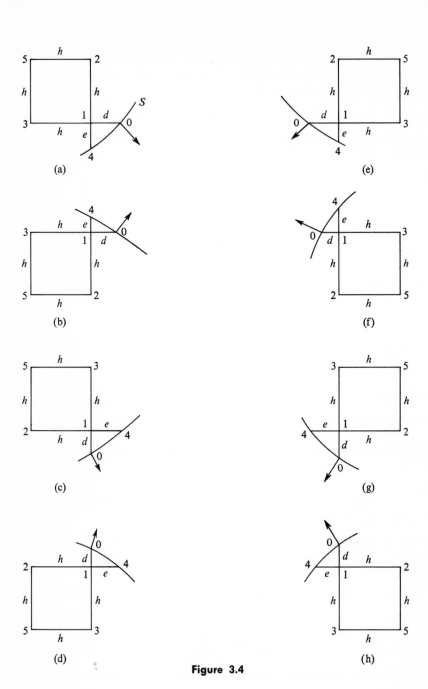

Figure 3.4

Thus, in order to approximate $\dfrac{\partial u}{\partial n}\Big|_0$, consider

(3.7)
$$\frac{\partial u}{\partial x}\Big|_0 \cos\alpha + \frac{\partial u}{\partial y}\Big|_0 \sin\alpha \equiv \sum_{i=0}^{5}\alpha_i u_i,$$

where the α_i's are to be determined. Assuming valid Taylor expansions for u_1, u_2, u_3, u_4, and u_5 about the point numbered 0 and substituting into (3.7), one finds

(3.8)
$$\frac{\partial u}{\partial x}\Big|_0 \cos\alpha + \frac{\partial u}{\partial y}\Big|_0 \sin\alpha \equiv u_0(\alpha_0 + \alpha_1 + \alpha_2 + \alpha_3 + \alpha_4 + \alpha_5)$$
$$+ \frac{\partial u}{\partial x}\Big|_0 [-d\alpha_1 - d\alpha_2 - (d+h)\alpha_3 - d\alpha_4 - (d+h)\alpha_5]$$
$$+ \frac{\partial u}{\partial y}\Big|_0 [h\alpha_2 - e\alpha_4 + h\alpha_5] + \frac{1}{2}\frac{\partial^2 u}{\partial x^2}\Big|_0 [d^2\alpha_1 + d^2\alpha_2 + (d+h)^2\alpha_3$$
$$+ d^2\alpha_4 + (d+h)^2\alpha_5]$$
$$+ \frac{\partial^2 u}{\partial x\,\partial y}\Big|_0 [-dh\alpha_2 + de\alpha_4 - 2h(h+d)\alpha_5] + \frac{1}{2}\frac{\partial^2 u}{\partial y^2}\Big|_0 [h^2\alpha_2 + e^2\alpha_4 + h^2\alpha_5]$$
$$+ O(\alpha_i h^3).$$

In order to make both sides of (3.8) agree in as many terms as possible, set the coefficients of u_0, $\dfrac{\partial u}{\partial x}\Big|_0$, $\dfrac{\partial u}{\partial y}\Big|_0$, $\dfrac{\partial^2 u}{\partial x^2}\Big|_0$, $\dfrac{\partial^2 u}{\partial x\,\partial y}\Big|_0$, and $\dfrac{\partial^2 u}{\partial y^2}\Big|_0$ on the left side of (3.8) equal to the corresponding coefficients on the right side and solve for α_0, α_1, α_2, α_3, α_4, α_5 to yield

(3.9)
$$\alpha_0 = \frac{h+2d}{d(h+d)}\cos\alpha, \quad \alpha_1 = -\frac{he(h+d)\cos\alpha + [hde - h^2 d + d^2 e]\sin\alpha}{h^2 de},$$

$$\alpha_2 = \frac{dh+eh+de}{h^2(e+h)}\sin\alpha, \quad \alpha_3 = \frac{dh\cos\alpha + d(d+h)\sin\alpha}{h^2(d+h)},$$

$$\alpha_4 = -\frac{h}{e(e+h)}\sin\alpha, \quad \alpha_5 = -\frac{d}{h^2}\sin\alpha.$$

Thus

(3.10)
$$\sum_{i=0}^{5}\alpha_i u_i = \frac{\partial u}{\partial n}\Big|_0,$$

where the α_i are given by (3.9), is the desired approximation.

TABLE 3.1

Figure	Changes To Be Made In (3.9)
3.4b	Replace sin α by $-\sin \alpha$
3.4c	Replace cos α by $-\sin \alpha$ and sin α by $-\cos \alpha$
3.4d	Replace cos α by sin α and sin α by $-\cos \alpha$
3.4e	Replace cos α by $-\cos \alpha$
3.4f	Replace sin α by $-\sin \alpha$ and cos α by $-\cos \alpha$
3.4g	Replace cos α by $-\sin \alpha$ and sin α by cos α
3.4h	Replace sin α by cos α and cos α by sin α

Analogous arguments or arguments using symmetry for the point patterns of Figures 3.4b–3.4h yield results which are summarized in the following simple way. In each case the approximation is of form (3.10). Recorded in Table 3.1 in the left hand column is the point pattern under consideration while in the right hand column are indicated the changes to be made in (3.9) in order to have the correct α_i's for the pattern.

3.3. THE NUMERICAL METHODS

Two numerical methods, called Method M_1 and Method M_2, will be described now for approximating solutions of the Mixed Problem.

Method M_1

Step 1. For fixed $h > 0$ and fixed $(\bar{x},\bar{y}) \in S^*$, construct G_h, R_h, $S_h = S_h^* \cup S_h'$.

Step 2. Suppose R_h consists of m points, S_h' consists of n_1 points, and S_h^* consists of n_2 points, so that G_h contains $m + n_1 + n_2$ points. Number the points of R_h in a one-to-one fashion with the integers $1 - m$ in such a way that the numbers are increasing from left to right on any horizontal line of the lattice and increasing from bottom to top on any vertical line of the lattice. Number the points of S_h' in a one-to-one fashion with the integers $m + 1, m + 2, \cdots, m + n_1$, and number the points of S_h^* in a one-to-one fashion with the integers $m + n_1 + 1, \cdots, m + n_1 + n_2$.

Step 3. At each point $(x,y) \in S_h^*$, set $U(x,y) = f(x,y)$. If (x,y) is numbered k then, in subscript notation, this is equivalent to $U_k = f(x,y)$.

Step 4. At each point (x,y) of R_h, beginning with the one numbered 1 and continuing in consecutive order through the one numbered m, write down the Laplace difference analogue

$$(3.11) \qquad -\left(\frac{2}{h_1 h_3} + \frac{2}{h_2 h_4}\right) U(x,y) + \frac{2}{h_1(h_1 + h_3)} U(x + h_1, y)$$

$$+ \frac{2}{h_2(h_2 + h_4)} U(x, y + h_2) + \frac{2}{h_3(h_1 + h_3)} U(x - h_3, y)$$

$$+ \frac{2}{h_4(h_2 + h_4)} U(x, y - h_4) = 0,$$

where, if any of the neighbors $(x + h_1, y)$, $(x, y + h_2)$, $(x - h_3, y)$, $(x, y - h_4)$ of (x,y) is a point of S_h^*, then U at this point is to be replaced by the known value f determined in Step 3. In practice, of course, these equations should be written in subscript notation.

Step 5. At each point $(x,y) \in S_h'$ of the types shown in Figures 3.1a and 3.1c, write down in subscript notation the equation

$$(3.12) \qquad \frac{U_0 - U_1}{d} = g(x,y)$$

and, at each point $(x,y) \in S_h'$ of the type shown in Figure 3.1b, write down in subscript notation the equation

$$(3.13) \qquad \frac{U_0}{d} - \frac{d_2}{d(d_2 + d_3)} U_3 - \frac{d_3}{d(d_2 + d_3)} U_2 = g(x,y).$$

Of course, wherever possible insert the known values determined in Step 3.

Step 6. Solve the linear algebraic system generated by Steps 4 and 5 for the unknowns $U_1, U_2, \cdots, U_{m+n_1}$.

Step 7. Let the values $U_1, U_2, \cdots, U_{m+n_1+n_2}$ found in Steps 3 and 6 represent the approximate solution of the Mixed Problem on G_h.

Method M_2

This method is the same as Method M_1 except for Step 5, which is modified as follows.

Step 5. For each point $(x,y) \in S_h'$ of the type shown in Figure 3.3, set down an equation of the form

$$\sum_0^2 \alpha_i U_i = g(x,y),$$

where, from (3.6),

$$\alpha_0 = \frac{h + 2d}{d(h + d)}, \quad \alpha_1 = -\frac{h + d}{hd}, \quad \alpha_2 = \frac{d}{h(h + d)}.$$

For each point $(x,y) \in S_h'$ of the type shown in Figure 3.4a, set down an equation of the type

(3.14) $$\sum_0^5 \alpha_i U_i = g(x,y),$$

where the α_i are given by (3.9). For each of the various other points of S_h', as displayed in Figures 3.4b–3.4h, set down an equation of the type

(3.15) $$\sum_0^5 \alpha_i U_i = g(x,y),$$

where the α_i are those which have been appropriately recorded in Table 3.1.

In the next two sections it will be shown how radically different are the implications of applying Methods M_1 and M_2. Note immediately, however, with regard to the matrices of the resulting linear algebraic systems that for Method M_1 one has diagonal dominance, which suggests the applicability of iteration methods for solving the system, while for Method M_2 there is no diagonal dominance. Moreover, for both methods the matrices are not, in general, symmetric.

3.4. THEORY FOR METHOD M_1

It will be shown now that Method M_1 is a reasonable numerical technique in that the associated linear algebraic system has a unique solution and that convergence of the numerical to the analytical solution results for a large class of Mixed Problems.

Theorem 3.1
The linear algebraic system generated by Method M_1 has a unique solution.

Proof:

The fundamental idea of the proof is the one applied in Theorem 2.2. Suppose then $f \equiv g \equiv 0$ and that there exists in addition to the zero solution, a nonzero solution of the linear algebraic system. At some point (x^*, y^*), assume without loss of generality that

$$(3.16) \qquad\qquad U(x^*, y^*) > 0$$

and that

$$(3.17) \quad U(x^*, y^*) \geq U_i,$$
$$i = 1, 2, \cdots, m, m+1, \cdots, m+n_1, \cdots, m+n_1+n_2.$$

Now, (x^*, y^*) cannot be a point of S_h^*, for if $(x,y) \in S_h^*$ then $U(x,y) = 0$. Moreover, (x^*, y^*) cannot be a point of R_h, for if it were then by the march to the boundary technique and the assumption that R_h is discretely connected, one could show that $0 = U(\bar{x}, \bar{y}) = U(x^*, y^*) > 0$, where $(\bar{x}, \bar{y})$ is that point used initially for the construction of G_h and hence is a point of S^*. Hence, $(x^*, y^*) \in S_h'$. But, if $(x^*, y^*) \in S_h'$, then $g \equiv 0$ and (3.12) imply $U(x^*, y^*) = U_1$, while $g \equiv 0$, (3.13), (3.17), and Lemma 2.2 imply $U(x^*, y^*) = U_2 = U_3$. Thus, if $(x^*, y^*) \in S_h'$, in all cases one finds that at some point of R_h one has $U = U(x^*, y^*)$, which, as shown above, leads to a contradiction. The theorem now follows readily by contradiction.

With regard to convergence, some valuable methods will be adapted next that were first devised by Gerschgorin [2] and later extended by Batschelet [1]. For this purpose, in addition to the operator $\mathscr{D}_h^{(1)}$ defined in (2.33), we shall need the following linear operators. For arbitrary $V(x,y)$, if $(x,y) \in S_h'$, is numbered 0, and is of the type shown in Figure 3.1a or 3.1c, then let

$$(3.18) \qquad\qquad \mathscr{D}_h^{(2)}[V(x,y)] = -\frac{V_0 - V_1}{d};$$

if $(x,y) \in S_h'$, is numbered 0, and is of the type shown in Figure 3.1b, then let

$$(3.19) \quad \mathscr{D}_h^{(3)}[V(x,y)] \equiv -\frac{V_0}{d} + \frac{d_2}{d(d_2 + d_3)} V_3 + \frac{d_3}{d(d_2 + d_3)} V_2;$$

and if $(x,y) \in S_h^*$ and is numbered 0, then let

$$(3.20) \qquad\qquad \mathscr{D}_h^{(4)}[V(x,y)] = -V_0.$$

Note that the following biunique correspondences exist between operators and sets: $\mathscr{D}_h^{(1)} \leftrightarrow R_h$; $\mathscr{D}_h^{(2)} \leftrightarrow$ Figure 3.1a and 3.1c type points of S_h'; $\mathscr{D}_h^{(3)} \leftrightarrow$ Figure 3.1b type points of S_h'; and $\mathscr{D}_h^{(4)} \leftrightarrow S_h^*$. Throughout, then, if operator $\mathscr{D}_h^{(i)}$, $i = 1, 2, 3,$ or 4, is associated with a point (x,y), it will be assumed that (x,y) is an element of the set defined by these correspondences.

Lemma 3.1

Let $z(x,y)$ be defined on G_h. If $\mathscr{D}_h^{(j)}[z(x,y)] \geq 0$, $j = 1, 2, 3, 4$, at each $(x,y) \in G_h$, then $z(x,y) \leq 0$ on G_h.

Proof:

Assume there exists $(x,y) \in G_h$ at which $z(x,y) > 0$. Since G_h is a finite set, there exists $(x^*,y^*) \in G_h$ at which $z(x^*,y^*) = z^* > 0$, where $z^* = \max_{G_h} z(x,y)$. By Lemma 2.1 it follows readily that $z(\bar{x},\bar{y}) = z^* > 0$, where $(\bar{x},\bar{y})$ is the point described in Step 1 of Method M_1. Hence, $\mathscr{D}_h^{(4)}[z(\bar{x},\bar{y})] = -z^* < 0$, which is a contradiction, and the lemma is proved.

Lemma 3.2

If $v(x,y)$, $w(x,y)$ are defined on G_h and $\mathscr{D}_h^{(j)}[w] \leq \mathscr{D}_h^{(j)}[v]$, $j = 1, 2, 3, 4$, at each $(x,y) \in G_h$, then $w(x,y) \geq v(x,y)$ on G_h.

Proof:

Set $z(x,y) = v(x,y) - w(x,y)$. Since $\mathscr{D}_h^{(1)}$, $\mathscr{D}_h^{(2)}$, $\mathscr{D}_h^{(3)}$, and $\mathscr{D}_h^{(4)}$ are linear, the proof is an immediate consequence of Lemma 3.1.

Lemma 3.3

If $v(x,y)$, $w(x,y)$ are defined on G_h and

$$\mathscr{D}_h^{(j)}[w(x,y)] \leq - |\mathscr{D}_h^{(j)}[v(x,y)]|, \qquad j = 1, 2, 3, 4,$$

at each $(x,y) \in G_h$, then $w(x,y) \geq |v(x,y)|$ on G_h.

Proof:

If $\mathscr{D}_h^{(j)}[w(x,y)] \leq - |\mathscr{D}_h^{(j)}[v(x,y)]|$, then $\mathscr{D}_h^{(j)}[w] \leq \mathscr{D}_h^{(j)}[v]$ and $\mathscr{D}_h^{(j)}[w] \leq \mathscr{D}_h^{(j)}[-v]$. By Lemma 3.2, then, $w \geq v$ on G_h and $w \geq -v$ on G_h, so that $w \geq |v|$ on G_h, and the lemma is proved.

It is convenient now to introduce an auxiliary error function $E^{(i)}$ defined by

(3.21) $E^{(i)} = u_i - U_i, \qquad i = 1, 2, \cdots, m + n_1 + n_2.$

From (2.61) and (3.21), then,

(3.22) $E(G_h) = \max_{(x,y)\epsilon G_h} |E^{(i)}| = \max_{(x,y)\epsilon G_h} |u_i - U_i|.$

Let us next approximate, in turn, $|\mathscr{D}_h^{(j)} E^{(i)}|, j = 1, 2, 3, 4.$ Thus,

(3.23) $\mathscr{D}_h^{(1)}[E^{(0)}] = \mathscr{D}_h^{(1)}[u_0] - \mathscr{D}_h^{(1)}[U_0]$

$$= -\left(\frac{2}{h_1 h_3} + \frac{2}{h_2 h_4}\right)u_0 + \frac{2}{h_1(h_1 + h_3)}u_1$$

$$+ \frac{2}{h_2(h_2 + h_4)}u_2 + \frac{2}{h_3(h_1 + h_3)}u_3$$

$$+ \frac{2}{h_4(h_2 + h_4)}u_4.$$

Assume now that u_1, u_2, u_3, u_4 have Taylor expansions through third order terms on G and define $M_i(u)$ by

(3.24) $M_i(u) = \max_G \left|\frac{\partial^i u}{\partial x^j \partial y^{i-j}}\right|,$

where i, j are nonnegative integers and $i \geq j$. Then insertion of Taylor expansions into (3.23) and use of $\Delta u \equiv 0$ and the notation of (3.24) imply

$$|\mathscr{D}_h^{(1)}[E^{(0)}]| \leq \frac{M_3(u)}{3}\left[\frac{h_1^2}{h_1 + h_3} + \frac{h_2^2}{h_2 + h_4} + \frac{h_3^2}{h_1 + h_3} + \frac{h_4^2}{h_2 + h_4}\right]$$

$$\leq \frac{M_3(u)}{3}[h_1 + h_2 + h_3 + h_4],$$

so that

$$|\mathscr{D}_h^{(1)}[E^{(0)}]| \leq \frac{4hM_3(u)}{3}.$$

Thus it follows immediately that on R_h

(3.25) $|\mathscr{D}_h^{(1)}[E^{(i)}]| \leq \frac{4hM_3(u)}{3}.$

Also

$$\mathscr{D}_h^{(2)}[E^{(0)}] = \mathscr{D}_h^{(2)}[u_0] - \mathscr{D}_h^{(2)}[U_0]$$

$$= -\frac{u_0 - u_1}{d} + g_0.$$

Insertion of a finite Taylor expansion through second order terms for u_1 implies

$$|\mathscr{D}_h^{(2)}[E^{(0)}]| \leq 2dM_2(u)$$

and hence that

(3.26) $$|\mathscr{D}_h^{(2)}[E^{(i)}]| \leq 2dM_2(u).$$

Next,

$$\mathscr{D}_h^{(3)}[E^{(0)}] = \mathscr{D}_h^{(3)}[u_0] - \mathscr{D}_h^{(3)}[U_0]$$

$$= -\frac{u_0}{d} + \frac{d_2}{d(d_2 + d_3)} u_3 + \frac{d_3}{d(d_2 + d_3)} u_2 + g_0.$$

Insertion of finite Taylor expansions for u_2 and u_3 implies

$$|\mathscr{D}_h^{(3)}[E^{(0)}]| \leq M_2(u)\left[2d + \frac{d_2 d_3}{2d}\right] \leq M_2(u)\left[2d + \frac{h}{2}\right],$$

so that

(3,27) $$|\mathscr{D}_h^{(3)}[E^{(i)}]| \leq M_2(u)\left[2d + \frac{h}{2}\right].$$

Finally,

$$\mathscr{D}_h^{(4)}[E^{(0)}] = \mathscr{D}_h^{(4)}[u_0] - \mathscr{D}_h^{(4)}[U_0] = 0,$$

so that

(3.28) $$\mathscr{D}_h^{(4)}[E^{(i)}] = 0.$$

Note that in (3.25)–(3.28) the correspondence described above between operators $\mathscr{D}_h^{(i)}$ and point sets is constantly in use.

The following theorem now establishes convergence for a large class of Mixed Problems.

Theorem 3.2

Let $z(x,y)$ be the unique function (consult Lichtenstein [1]) which has the properties

(3.29) $$z_{xx} + z_{yy} \equiv -1 \qquad \text{on } R$$

(3.30) $$z \equiv 1 \qquad \text{on } S^*$$

(3.31) $$\frac{\partial z}{\partial n} \equiv 1 \qquad \text{on } S'.$$

If $z(x,y) \in C^3(G)$ and if the analytical solution u of the Mixed Problem is of class $C^3(G)$, then it follows that

$$\lim_{h \to 0} E(G_h) = \lim_{h \to 0} \max_{(x,y) \in G_h} |E^{(i)}| = 0.$$

Proof:

The major portion of the proof will be devoted to relating $E^{(i)}$ to $z(x,y)$. This will be done by constructing a positive m, independent of x and y, so that

(3.32) $$\max |E^{(i)}| \leq w(x,y) \equiv m\, z(x,y), \qquad m \geq 0.$$

Now, (3.32) would be valid, by Lemma 3.3, if

(3.33) $$\mathscr{D}_h^{(j)}[w] \leq -|\mathscr{D}_h^{(j)}[E^{(i)}]|, \qquad j = 1, 2, 3, 4$$

and so we are led to consider four cases.

Case 1. By substitution of finite Taylor expansions through third order terms, it follows from (3.29) that for all sufficiently small h

(3.34)
$$\mathscr{D}_h^{(1)}[w_0] = m\mathscr{D}_h^{(1)}[z_0] = m[z_{xx} + z_{yy} + 0(h)] \leq m\left[-1 + \frac{1}{2}\right] = -\frac{m}{2}.$$

Thus (3.25), (3.33), and (3.34) imply that we wish to choose m so that

(3.35) $$m \geq \frac{8}{3} hM_3(u).$$

Case 2. By substitution of finite Taylor expansions through second order terms, it follows from (3.31) for all sufficiently small h that

(3.36) $$\mathscr{D}_h^{(2)}[w_0] \leq m\left[-1 + \frac{1}{2}\right] = -\frac{m}{2}.$$

Thus (3.26), (3.33), and (3.36) imply that we wish to choose m so that

(3.37) $$m \geq 4dM_2(u).$$

Case 3. By substitution of finite Taylor expansions through second order terms, it follows from (3.31) for all sufficiently small h that

(3.38) $$\mathscr{D}_h^{(3)}[w_0] \leq m\left[-1 + \frac{1}{2}\right] = -\frac{m}{2}.$$

Thus (3.27), (3.33), and (3.38) imply that we wish to choose m so that

(3.39) $$m \geq [4d + h]M_2(u).$$

Case 4. Since $\mathscr{D}_h^{(4)}[w_0] = -w_0 = -mz_0 = -m$, it follows from (3.28) that any choice of $m \geq 0$ would satisfy (3.33).

Thus, define m by

(3.40) $$m = \max \left[(4d + h)M_2(u), \frac{8}{3} h\, M_3(u) \right].$$

Then, on G_h, $\mathscr{D}_h^{(j)}[w] = \mathscr{D}_h^{(j)}[mz] \leq - |\mathscr{D}_h^{(j)}[E^{(i)}]|$, so that, on G_h

(3.41) $$|E^{(i)}| \leq mz$$

and

(3.42) $$E(G_h) = \max [E^{(i)}] \leq \max [mz].$$

But z is bounded on G and $m \to 0$ as $h \to 0$, so that (3.42) implies the validity of the theorem.

3.5. THEORY FOR METHOD M_2

No general theorems on uniqueness and convergence comparable to those for Method M_1 can be established for Method M_2. The reason for this is that the linear algebraic system generated by the second method need not have a solution or, indeed, may have more than one solution, as will be shown below. This pathological behavior, it seems, can appear whenever a second order method is used to approximate normal derivatives by methods that conform to the spirit of Section 3.1.

Consider then the following example. For the domain G whose boundary is S and whose interior is R, as shown in Figure 3.5, let $(\bar{x}, \bar{y}) = (0,0)$, $h = 2$, so that R_h consists of the points numbered 1, 2, and S_h consists of the points numbered 3–8. Let S' be the subarc of S which has the points numbered 9 and 10 for end points and contains the points numbered 3 and 4. On $S^* = S - S'$ define

(3.43) $$f(x,y) = xy$$

and on S' define

(3.44) $$g(x,y) = 0.$$

Also, let the angles of the normals at the points numbered 3 and 4 be given by $\alpha = 45°$ and $\beta = \tan^{-1} \frac{2}{11}$, respectively. Then, by Method M_2, one has first that

(3.45) $$U_5 = U_7 = U_8 = 0, \quad U_6 = -2.$$

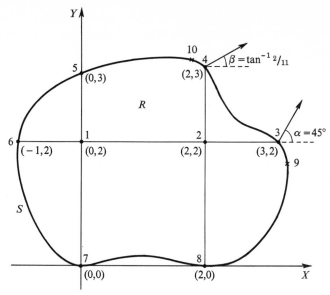

Figure 3.5

Corresponding to the points 1 and 2 there then result the equations

(3.46) $-2U_1 + \tfrac{1}{3}U_2 - \tfrac{4}{3} = 0$

and

(3.47) $\tfrac{1}{3}U_1 - 2U_2 + \tfrac{2}{3}U_3 + \tfrac{2}{3}U_4 = 0,$

while corresponding to the points numbered 3 and 4 there result the equations

(3.48) $-\dfrac{\sqrt{2}}{24} U_1 - \dfrac{7\sqrt{2}}{8} U_2 + \dfrac{2\sqrt{2}}{3} U_3 + \dfrac{\sqrt{2}}{3} U_4 = 0$

and

(3.49) $-\dfrac{11}{12\sqrt{5}} U_1 - \dfrac{23}{20\sqrt{5}} U_2 + \dfrac{22}{15\sqrt{5}} U_3 + \dfrac{8}{15\sqrt{5}} U_4 = 0.$

Unfortunately, the determinant of system (3.46)–(3.49) is zero and it can be shown easily that the system has no solution. Of course, the example can be modified by setting $f(x,y) = x^2y + xy$ to yield in a similar fashion a linear algebraic system which has more than one solution.

Regardless of the above discussion, the possible applicability of Method M_2 to yield better results than Method M_1 should not be discounted. This will be demonstrated by the examples in the next section and will imply strongly a need to examine the condition of the coefficient matrix when applying Method M_2.

3.6. EXAMPLES AND REMARKS

Each of the following examples was run on the CDC 1604.

Example 1. Let R be the interior of the unit circle $S: x^2 + y^2 = 1$ (see Figure 3.6). S^* is defined to be those points of S for which $y \leq 0$ so that S' is that set of points of S for which $y > 0$. The problem is to approximate that unique solution of the Mixed Problem which is of class $C^3(G)$ and for which

(3.50) $f(x,y) = x^3 - 3xy^2,$ $(x,y) \in S^*$

(3.51) $g(x,y) = 3x^3 - 9xy^2,$ $(x,y) \in S'.$

The lattice was constructed with $(\bar{x},\bar{y}) = (0, -1)$ and $h = .125$. Method M_1 was applied. The resulting 222 algebraic equations were solved by Gauss elimination and the running time was 2 minutes. Typical results are recorded under $U^{(1)}$ of Table 3.2.

Example 2. All the details were the same as in Example 1 except that the linear algebraic system was solved by Gauss–Seidel iteration with zero initial vector. The running time was approximately 2 minutes and the results to five decimal places were the same as those obtained in Example 1.

Example 3. All details were the same as in Example 1 except that Method M_2 was applied. The linear algebraic system was solved by Gauss elimination and the running time was approximately 2 minutes. Typical results are recorded under $U^{(2)}$ of Table 3.2. Note that the results at most points were better than those obtained in Examples 1 and 2 and that even though methods for improving the condition of a matrix (Eisemann [1], Forsythe and Motzkin [1], Mendelsohn [1]) were readied, the need for their application did not arise.

Example 4. All details were the same as in Example 3 except that the linear algebraic system was solved by Gauss–Seidel iteration with zero initial vector and the running time was approximately 9 minutes. The results agreed to five decimal places with those of Example 3.

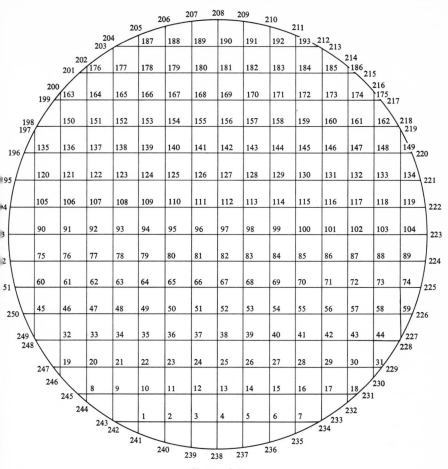

Figure 3.6

Example 5. All details were the same as in Example 3 except that successive over-relaxation was applied to the linear algebraic system with $\omega = 1.8$ and zero initial vector. The iteration diverged.

Example 6. All the details were the same as in Example 1 except that the grid size was decreased by a factor of one half. The resulting linear algebraic equations were solved by Gauss–Seidel iteration with zero initial vector in 37 minutes and the results were better than $U^{(1)}$ but, except at isolated points, still not as good as $U^{(2)}$.

TABLE 3.2

Point Number	$U^{(1)}$	$U^{(2)}$	Exact Solution $u = x^3 - 3xy^2$
1	.80875	.80872	.80859
4	.00000	.00000	.00000
11	.40654	.40642	.40625
14	−.20915	−.20907	−.20898
23	.27787	.27762	.27734
29	−.46159	−.46135	−.46094
33	.22554	.22525	.22461
44	−.14124	−.14113	−.14063
46	−.10446	−.10460	−.10547
50	.09120	.09048	.08984
56	−.08767	−.08694	−.08594
60	−.50520	−.50490	−.50586
67	.00000	.00000	.00000
71	.02858	.02978	.03125
83	−.00571	−.00456	−.00391
89	.62894	.62757	.62891
90	−.67252	−.66768	−.66992
99	.01055	.01392	.01563
103	.42037	.41874	.42188
108	−.09092	−.09743	−.10156
118	.38451	.38172	.38672
122	−.11086	−.12033	−.12695
125	.04295	.03417	.03125
130	−.03326	−.02185	−.01758
133	.27053	.27361	.28125
135	−.28056	−.28644	−.30078
137	.04729	.02811	.01953
138	.11316	.09294	.08594
145	−.12894	−.11085	−.10547
155	.10449	.09407	.09180
161	−.26716	−.23478	−.22461
166	.43411	.39471	.38672
169	.00000	.00000	.00000
191	−.31652	−.28909	−.28516
195	−.74214	−.71913	−.72618
201	.91554	.84076	.82680
203	1.11900	1.01699	1.00000
208	.00000	.00000	.00000
215	−.91554	−.84076	−.82680

Finally it should be noted that other methods for Mixed Problems have been explored by Allen and Robins [1], Batschelet [1], Edwards [1,2], Fox [1], Friedrichs [1], Lebedev [1], Varga [1], and Viswanathan [1].

EXERCISES

1. Consider the Mixed Problem given in Exercise 24 of Chapter 1. Find numerical approximations by both Methods M_1 and M_2 for each of the following.

(a) $(\bar{x},\bar{y}) = (0,0)$, $h = .25.$
(b) $(\bar{x},\bar{y}) = (0,0)$, $h = .2.$
(c) $(\bar{x},\bar{y}) = (0,0)$, $h = .1.$

In each case compare the numerical results with the exact solution $u = x^2 - y^2$.

2. Let R be the interior of the unit circle S: $x^2 + y^2 = 1$. S^* is defined to be those points of S for which $y \leq 0$, so that S' is that set of points of S for which $y > 0$. Find approximations by both Methods M_1 and M_2 to the Mixed Problem with $f(x,y) = x^3 - 3xy^2$, $g(x,y) = 3x^3 - 9xy^2$ for each of the following.

(a) $(\bar{x},\bar{y}) = (0,0)$, $h = .5.$
(b) $(\bar{x},\bar{y}) = (0,0)$, $h = .3.$
(c) $(\bar{x},\bar{y}) = (0,0)$, $h = .2.$
(d) $(\bar{x},\bar{y}) = (0,0)$, $h = .1.$
(e) $(\bar{x},\bar{y}) = (0,1)$, $h = .4.$

In each case compare the numerical results with the exact solution $u = x^3 - 3xy^2$.

3. With regard to Figure 3.4a, discuss the possibility of deriving a second order approximation for $\dfrac{\partial u}{\partial n}$ at the point numbered 0 by taking into account the values of u only at the points numbered 0–4.

4. With regard to Figure3. 4a, discuss the possilibity of deriving a third order approximation for $\dfrac{\partial u}{\partial n}$ at the point numbered 0 by taking into account values of u at *additional* points besides 0–5 of G_h.

5. Calculate $\mathscr{D}_h^{(2)}$, $\mathscr{D}_h^{(3)}$ and $\mathscr{D}_h^{(4)}$ for each of the following.

(a) $V(x,y) = 5.$ (d) $V(x,y) = x^7 - x^3y - 3.$
(b) $V(x,y) = 2y.$ (e) $V(x,y) = e^{-xy}.$
(c) $V(x,y) = x^2 - y^3.$ (f) $V(x,y) = y \sin x.$

6. Generalize Methods M_1 and M_2 by introducing a rectangular rather than a square grid (see Exercise 8, Chapter 2).

7. For Mixed Problems in which S is a circle, devise a numerical method which utilizes polar coordinates. Discuss the assets and liabilities of your method.

CHAPTER 4

DIRICHLET AND MIXED PROBLEMS FOR MORE GENERAL TWO DIMENSIONAL LINEAR ELLIPTIC EQUATIONS

4.1. INTRODUCTION

The Dirichlet and Mixed Problems can be extended in a variety of ways so that those problems defined in Chapter 1 are special cases of more general ones. One could assume first that R is not necessarily simply connected. The numerical methods already described would then be applicable without change. However, not all such problems are well posed and one would have to exercise care to be assured that any particular analytical problem had a unique solution (consult, e.g., Petrovsky [2], p. 187). Second, if one were to generalize by considering boundary conditions of the form

$$(4.1) \qquad v(s)f + w(s)\frac{\partial u}{\partial n} = z(s),$$

where f and $\dfrac{\partial u}{\partial n}$ are prescribed and continuous on S, s is arc length, and v, w, and, z are defined arbitrarily on S, then the numerical methods already given extend easily by merely substituting into (4.1) one of the normal derivative approximations already developed. Again, however, one must be exceptionally careful that the specific analytical problem is well posed (see, e.g., Lichtenstein [2], and Visik and Ladyzenskaya [1]). Third, since no use of normality was made in the derivation in Section 3.2, nor in the theoretical considerations of Section 3.3, it follows that the formulas

57

developed also apply to problems in which oblique, or directional, derivatives are prescribed on the boundary. (Concerning existence and uniqueness of solutions of problems of this type, see, e.g., Vekua [1], and Visik and Ladyzenskaya [1].) Thus, for Dirichlet and Mixed Problems no essential *numerical* difficulty is introduced by generalizing the nature of *G* or the boundary conditions in the ways indicated above.

It is natural, however, that if the Laplace equation were to be replaced by a more complex elliptic equation, then the corresponding difference analogue would also increase in complexity. Attention, therefore, will be directed toward constructing difference analogues of elliptic equations which are more general than Laplace's equation. And at least in the case where the coefficients of (1.2) are constant, the numerical methods already developed need be modified only in a natural way by replacing (2.7) with the new analogue developed.

The following definitions will be fundamental for the development.

Definition 4.1

Let $(x,y) \in R_h$ and let its neighbors be arranged and numbered as in Figure 1.1. With regard to (1.2), let the linear operator $\mathscr{D}$ be defined for all $u \in C^2(R)$ by

$$\mathscr{D}[u] = Au_{xx} + 2Bu_{xy} + Cu_{yy} + Du_x + Eu_y + Fu$$

and let linear operator $\mathscr{D}_h$ be defined by

$$\mathscr{D}_h[u] = \sum_0^4 \alpha_i u_i.$$

Then $\mathscr{D}_h$ is said to be a five-point operator approximation of $\mathscr{D}$ at (x,y) iff

$$\lim_{h \to 0} \{ \mathscr{D}[u(x,y)] - \mathscr{D}_h[u(x,y)] \} = 0.$$

Definition 4.2

In the terminology of Definition 4.1, any equation algebraically equivalent to

$$\mathscr{D}_h[u(x,y)] = 0$$

is said to be a five-point difference analogue or difference equation approximation of $\mathscr{D}[u(x,y)] = 0$ at (x,y) iff $\mathscr{D}_h[u]$ is a five-point operator approximation of $\mathscr{D}$ at (x,y).

Definition 4.3

If $\mathcal{D}_h[u]$ is a five-point operator approximation of $\mathcal{D}[u]$ at (x,y), then any equation algebraically equivalent to

$$\mathcal{D}_h[u] + G_0 = 0$$

is said to be a five-point difference analogue or difference equation approximation of

$$\mathcal{D}[u(x,y)] + G(x,y) = 0$$

i.e., of (1.2) at (x,y).

4.2. THE GENERAL LINEAR ELLIPTIC DIFFERENTIAL EQUATION WITH CONSTANT COEFFICIENTS

It is known (see, e.g., Greenspan [6]) with regard to (1.2) that if A, B, C, D, E, F are constants, then a constructible linear transformation can be given under which the transformed equation has no u_{xy} term and that under such a transformation the elliptic character of the equation is preserved. Thus, without loss of generality consider first, for A, B, C, D, E, F constants, the equation

$$(4.2) \qquad Au_{xx} + Cu_{yy} + Du_x + Eu_y + Fu + G = 0$$

with the ellipticity condition

$$(4.3) \qquad\qquad\qquad -AC < 0.$$

It is also known (see, e.g., Courant and Hilbert [1]) that if $AF \le 0$, then any solution of (4.2) subject to (4.3) possesses a weak max–min property, so that it will be assumed further that

$$(4.4) \qquad\qquad\qquad A > 0,\, C > 0,\, F \le 0.$$

(Note of course that (4.4) implies (4.3).)

In order to construct a five-point difference analogue of (4.2), consider the same five-point arrangement as shown in Figure 2.1 and treated in Section 2.2, and set

$$(4.5) \qquad Au_{xx} + Cu_{yy} + Du_x + Eu_y + Fu \equiv \sum_0^4 \alpha_i u_i.$$

Substitution of finite Taylor expansions about (x,y) into (4.5) implies, analogous to (2.4), that

$$\alpha_0 + \alpha_1 + \alpha_2 + \alpha_3 + \alpha_4 = F$$

$$h_1\alpha_1 - h_3\alpha_3 = D$$

$$h_2\alpha_2 - h_4\alpha_4 = E$$

$$h_1^2\alpha_1 + h_3^2\alpha_3 = 2A$$

$$h_2^2\alpha_2 + h_4^2\alpha_4 = 2C,$$

the solution of which is

$$\alpha_0 = \frac{Fh_1h_2h_3h_4 - 2Ah_2h_4 - 2Ch_1h_3 - Dh_2h_4(h_3 - h_1) - Eh_1h_3(h_2 - h_4)}{h_1h_2h_3h_4}$$

(4.6)
$$\alpha_1 = \frac{2A + Dh_3}{h_1(h_1 + h_3)}, \qquad \alpha_2 = \frac{2C - Eh_4}{h_2(h_2 + h_4)},$$

$$\alpha_3 = \frac{2A - Dh_1}{h_3(h_1 + h_3)}, \qquad \alpha_4 = \frac{2C - Eh_2}{h_4(h_2 + h_4)}.$$

Thus, with the α_i given in (4.6) one has

$$\mathscr{D}[u(x,y)] - \mathscr{D}_h[u(x,y)] \equiv \sum_1^4 [O(h_i)], \qquad 0 < h_i \le h,$$

from which it follows that $\mathscr{D}_h$ is a five-point operator approximation of $\mathscr{D}$ at (x,y). Thus, at (x,y) an analogue of (4.2) is

(4.7) $$\alpha_0 u_0 + \alpha_1 u_1 + \alpha_2 u_2 + \alpha_3 u_3 + \alpha_4 u_4 + G_0 = 0,$$

where the α_i are given by (4.6).

Now, the usual way to study (4.2) is to consider first the simpler elliptic equation

(4.2a) $$Au_{xx} + Cu_{yy} + Du_x + Eu_y + Fu = 0.$$

Following in this fashion then, one has from (4.7) that a difference analogue of this equation at (x,y) is

(4.7a) $$\alpha_0 u_0 + \alpha_1 u_1 + \alpha_2 u_2 + \alpha_3 u_3 + \alpha_4 u_4 = 0.$$

Observe next that $\sum_0^4 \alpha_i = F \le 0$, so that the coefficients of this difference analogue cannot in general satisfy the assumptions of the Star Lemma. Let us then attempt first to find an upper bound on h so that α_0, α_1, α_2, α_3,

α_4 satisfy the assumptions of Lemma 2.1 at each point of any R_h, which, in turn, will imply by Lemma 2.3 the existence of a weak max–min property for any solution on R_h of difference equation (4.7a).

Since α_1 is to be positive, consider with regard to (4.6)

$$2A > |D| h_3.$$

Then, if h satisfies

(4.8) $$2A > |D| h,$$

it follows easily that $\alpha_1 > 0$. Similarly, (4.8) implies $\alpha_3 > 0$. The assumption $\alpha_2 > 0$ in turn implies the desirability of

$$2C > |E| h_4.$$

Thus if h satisfies

(4.9) $$2C > |E| h,$$

then it follows that $\alpha_2 > 0$ and that $\alpha_4 > 0$. Thus, rewriting (4.8) and (4.9) in the equivalent form

(4.10) $$\max \left[\frac{h\,|D|}{2A}, \frac{h\,|E|}{2C} \right] < 1,$$

one has $\alpha_i > 0$, $i = 1, 2, 3, 4$. One need only show then that (4.10) implies $\alpha_0 < 0$, and this will now be done.

From (4.4) and (4.6),

$$\alpha_0 = \frac{Fh_1h_2h_3h_4 - 2Ah_2h_4 - 2Ch_1h_3 - Dh_2h_4(h_3 - h_1) - Eh_1h_3(h_2 - h_4)}{h_1h_2h_3h_4}$$

$$\leq \frac{-1}{h_1h_2h_3h_4} \{ h_2h_4[2A + D(h_3 - h_1)] + h_1h_3[2C + E(h_2 - h_4)] \}.$$

But, from (4.7) and (4.8),

$$0 < 2A - |D|\, h \leq 2A - |D|\, |h_1 - h_3| \leq 2A + D(h_3 - h_1)$$

and

$$0 < 2C - |E|\, h \leq 2C - |E|\, |h_2 - h_4| \leq 2C + E(h_2 - h_4),$$

from which it follows that $\alpha_0 < 0$.

Note that (4.10) actually allows one to determine h in a constructive fashion.

The above results are summarized by the following theorem.

Theorem 4.1

For any h, (4.7)—with coefficients α_i given by (4.6)—is a five-point difference analogue at (x,y) of (4.2). If, in addition, h satisfies (4.10), then the α_i, $i = 0$, 1, 2, 3, 4, of (4.6) satisfy the assumptions of Lemma 2.1 at every (x,y).

Now, in order to extend the theory of Chapters 2 and 3 to Dirichlet and Mixed Problems for (4.2), it appears natural to fix $(\bar{x},\bar{y})$, to select an h which satisfies (4.10), and to apply (4.7) at each point of R_h. And, as a matter of fact, the resulting numerical method then has a unique solution that converges to the analytical solution u provided $u \in C^2(R \cup S)$. The proofs are straightforward extensions of those in Chapters 2 and 3.

Note also that much has been written about difference analogues of linear elliptic equations with constant coefficients. For example, triangular, rectangular, hexagonal, and variable grids; five-point, nine-point, and many-point analogues; and high-order analogues that utilize derivatives have been treated carefully (consult, e.g., Allen and Dennis [1], Batschelet [1], Bickley [1], Bramble and Hubbard [1], Collatz [2], Davidenko[1, 2, 3, 4], Durand [1], Frocht [1], Greenspan [4, 9], Heilbronn [1], Korolyuk [1], Laasonen [1, 2, 3], Lyusternik [1, 2, 3], Mikeladze [1, 2, 3, 4, 5], Milne [2], Motzkin and Wasow [1], Rowe [1], and Volkov [3]). Further, analogues whose coefficients are not amenable to the application of Lemma 2.1 have also been studied (Bramble and Hubbard [2]).

4.3. LINEAR ELLIPTIC DIFFERENTIAL EQUATIONS WITH NONCONSTANT COEFFICIENTS

If the coefficients of (1.2) are continuous and bounded on R, the question of existence of difference analogues on some rectangular grid, with α_i's that satisfy the assumptions of Lemma 2.1, was answered in the affirmative by Motzkin and Wasow [1]. Their methods, however, were nonconstructive, so that neither the combination of points required nor a difference analogue itself was ever exhibited. Though the development here will be constructive, it will of necessity be severely restrictive and little more than introductory because the complexities involved are very great.

Attention will be restricted to the basic equation

$$(4.11) \qquad A(x,y)u_{xx} + 2B(x,y)u_{xy} + C(x,y)u_{yy} = 0,$$

where A, B, C are continuous and bounded on $G = R \cup S$ and the ellipticity condition

$$(4.12) \qquad\qquad B^2 - AC < 0$$

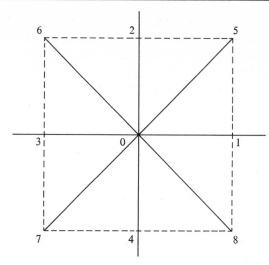

Figure 4.1

is valid on R. (In the next chapter an equation somewhat different from (4.11), but with a nonconstant coefficient, also will be treated, but from a different point of view.) Since (4.12) implies $A(x,y)$ is never zero, (4.11) can be written in the equivalent form

(4.13) $u_{xx} + 2b(x,y)u_{xy} + c(x,y)u_{yy} = 0,$

where, on R,

(4.14) $c(x,y) > 0,$

(4.15) $[b(x,y)]^2 - c(x,y) < 0,$

and

(4.16) $b = \dfrac{B}{A}, \quad c = \dfrac{C}{A}.$

Because it will be shown later that in general (4.13) and hence (4.11) do not possess five-point difference analogues whose coefficients satisfy the assumptions of Lemma 2.1, let us begin in a more general and rather heuristic fashion to develop some kind of analogue of (4.13). For $h > 0$, let the points (x,y), $(x + h, y)$, $(x, y + h)$, $(x - h, y)$, $(x, y - h)$, $(x + h, y + h)$, $(x - h, y + h)$, $(x - h, y - h)$, $(x + h, y - h)$ be denoted by the integers $0, 1, \cdots, 8$, respectively, as in Figure 4.1. Only those values of h

will be considered for which the points themselves and the line segments joining the point numbered 0 to each of the other points are also in R. As usual, let $u(x,y)$ at a point numbered i be denoted by u_i.

An attempt will be made to develop a difference analogue of (4.13) at (x,y) by use of *at most* the nine points described above. For this purpose, let the linear operator $\mathcal{K}$, defined for all $u \in C^2(R)$, be given by

$$(4.17) \qquad \mathcal{K}[u] = u_{xx} + 2bu_{xy} + cu_{yy}.$$

Motivated then by the special case where $h_1 = h_2 = h_3 = h_4 = h$ in (2.1) and (2.5), we define $\mathcal{K}_h$ by

$$(4.18) \qquad \mathcal{K}_h[u(x,y)] = h^{-2} \sum_{i=0}^{8} \alpha_i u_i$$

and seek to determine the α_i's such that each may depend on x and y, *but not on h or u*, and such that each of the following relationships (4.19)–(4.22) is valid at (x,y) for all $u \in C^2(R)$:

$$(4.19) \qquad \lim_{h \to 0} \{\mathcal{K}_h[u(x,y)] - \mathcal{K}[u(x,y)]\} = 0,$$

$$(4.20) \qquad \alpha_0 < 0, \quad \alpha_i > 0, \qquad i = 1, 2, 3, 4,$$

$$(4.21) \qquad \alpha_j \geq 0, \qquad j = 5, 6, 7, 8,$$

$$(4.22) \qquad \sum_{0}^{8} \alpha_i = 0.$$

Substitution into (4.18) of finite Taylor expansions about (x,y) for $u_1, u_2, \cdots, u_8$ readily implies

$$(4.23) \quad \mathcal{K}_h[u(x,y)] - \mathcal{K}[u(x,y)] =$$
$$h^{-2}u(x,y)[\alpha_0 + \alpha_1 + \alpha_2 + \alpha_3 + \alpha_4 + \alpha_5 + \alpha_6 + \alpha_7 + \alpha_8]$$
$$+ h^{-1}u_x(x,y)[\alpha_1 - \alpha_3 + \alpha_5 - \alpha_6 - \alpha_7 + \alpha_8]$$
$$+ h^{-1}u_y(x,y)[\alpha_2 - \alpha_4 + \alpha_5 + \alpha_6 - \alpha_7 - \alpha_8]$$
$$+ \frac{1}{2}[\alpha_1 u_{xx}(\gamma_1, y) + \alpha_3 u_{xx}(\gamma_2, y) + \alpha_5 u_{xx}(\gamma_3, \delta_3) + \alpha_6 u_{xx}(\gamma_4, \delta_4)$$
$$+ \alpha_7 u_{xx}(\gamma_5, \delta_5) + \alpha_8 u_{xx}(\gamma_6, \delta_6) - 2u_{xx}(x,y)]$$
$$+ [\alpha_5 u_{xy}(\gamma_3, \delta_3) - \alpha_6 u_{xy}(\gamma_4, \delta_4) + \alpha_7 u_{xy}(\gamma_5, \delta_5) - \alpha_8 u_{xy}(\gamma_6, \delta_6)$$
$$- 2b(x,y)u_{xy}(x,y)]$$
$$+ \frac{1}{2}[\alpha_2 u_{yy}(x, \delta_1) + \alpha_4 u_{yy}(x, \delta_2) + \alpha_5 u_{yy}(\gamma_3, \delta_3) + \alpha_6 u_{yy}(\gamma_4, \delta_4)$$
$$+ \alpha_7 u_{yy}(\gamma_5, \delta_5) + \alpha_8 u_{yy}(\gamma_6, \delta_6) - 2c(x, y)u_{yy}(x,y)],$$

where

(4.24) $x - h < \gamma_i < x + h, \quad y - h < \delta_i < y + h, \quad i = 1, 2, \cdots, 6.$

By the continuity of u_{xx}, u_{xy} and u_{yy}, however, (4.23) can be rewritten

(4.25) $\mathscr{K}_h[u(x,y)] - \mathscr{K}[u(x,y)] =$

$$h^{-2}u(x,y)[\alpha_0 + \alpha_1 + \alpha_2 + \alpha_3 + \alpha_4 + \alpha_5 + \alpha_6 + \alpha_7 + \alpha_8]$$
$$+ h^{-1}u_x(x,y)[\alpha_1 - \alpha_3 + \alpha_5 - \alpha_6 - \alpha_7 + \alpha_8]$$
$$+ h^{-1}u_y(x,y)[\alpha_2 - \alpha_4 + \alpha_5 + \alpha_6 - \alpha_7 - \alpha_8]$$
$$+ \frac{1}{2}u_{xx}(x,y)[\alpha_1 + \alpha_3 + \alpha_5 + \alpha_6 + \alpha_7 + \alpha_8 - 2]$$
$$+ u_{xy}(x,y)[\alpha_5 - \alpha_6 + \alpha_7 - \alpha_8 - 2b]$$
$$+ \frac{1}{2}u_{yy}(x,y)[\alpha_2 + \alpha_4 + \alpha_5 + \alpha_6 + \alpha_7 + \alpha_8 - 2c] + \epsilon,$$

where

(4.26) $$\lim_{h \to 0} \epsilon = 0.$$

But since u is an arbitrary function of class $C^2(R)$ and since $\alpha_0, \alpha_1, \cdots, \alpha_8$ are independent of h, substitution of $u = 1$ into (4.25) implies by (4.19) and (4.26) that

(4.27) $$\alpha_0 + \alpha_1 + \alpha_2 + \alpha_3 + \alpha_4 + \alpha_5 + \alpha_6 + \alpha_7 + \alpha_8 = 0.$$

Similarly, substitution of $u = x$ into (4.25) implies by (4.19), (4.26), and (4.27) that

(4.28) $$\alpha_1 - \alpha_3 + \alpha_5 - \alpha_6 - \alpha_7 + \alpha_8 = 0.$$

In an analogous fashion, substitution of the functions $u = y$, $u = x^2$ $u = xy$, and $u = y^2$, in turn, into (4.25) readily implies that

(4.29) $$\alpha_2 - \alpha_4 + \alpha_5 + \alpha_6 - \alpha_7 - \alpha_8 = 0,$$

(4.30) $$\alpha_1 + \alpha_3 + \alpha_5 + \alpha_6 + \alpha_7 + \alpha_8 = 2,$$

(4.31) $$\alpha_5 - \alpha_6 + \alpha_7 - \alpha_8 = 2b,$$

(4.32) $$\alpha_2 + \alpha_4 + \alpha_5 + \alpha_6 + \alpha_7 + \alpha_8 = 2c.$$

The unique solution of system (4.27)–(4.32) for $\alpha_0, \alpha_1, \cdots, \alpha_5$ in terms of $\alpha_6, \alpha_7, \alpha_8$ is given by

(4.33) $\alpha_0 = -2 - 2c + 2b + 2\alpha_6 + 2\alpha_8,$

(4.34) $\alpha_1 = 1 - 2b - \alpha_6 + \alpha_7 - 2\alpha_8,$

(4.35) $\alpha_2 = c - 2b - 2\alpha_6 + \alpha_7 - \alpha_8,$

(4.36) $\alpha_3 = 1 - \alpha_6 - \alpha_7,$

(4.37) $\alpha_4 = c - \alpha_7 - \alpha_8,$

(4.38) $\alpha_5 = 2b + \alpha_6 - \alpha_7 + \alpha_8.$

Note immediately that for a five-point analogue, whose coefficients satisfy the assumptions of Lemma 2.1, to exist it is necessary that $\alpha_5 = \alpha_6 = \alpha_7 = \alpha_8 = 0$, so that (4.38) would require that $b = 0$. This, however, need not be valid so that in general a five-point analogue does not exist.

It follows readily then from (4.33)–(4.38) that the problem of constructing $\mathscr{K}_h$ in (4.18) which satisfies (4.19)–(4.22) is equivalent to finding nonnegative $\alpha_6, \alpha_7, \alpha_8$ that satisfy

(4.39) $-2 - 2c + 2b + 2\alpha_6 + 2\alpha_8 < 0,$

(4.40) $1 - 2b - \alpha_6 + \alpha_7 - 2\alpha_8 > 0,$

(4.41) $c - 2b - 2\alpha_6 + \alpha_7 - \alpha_8 > 0,$

(4.42) $1 - \alpha_6 - \alpha_7 > 0,$

(4.43) $c - \alpha_7 - \alpha_8 > 0,$

and

(4.44) $2b + \alpha_6 - \alpha_7 + \alpha_8 \geq 0.$

With this equivalent formulation, we will now prove a fundamental theorem.

Theorem 4.2

At $(x,y) \in R$, a necessary and sufficient condition for a $\mathscr{K}_h$ of form (4.18) to exist that satisfies (4.19)–(4.22) is that

(4.45) $|b(x,y)| < \min\,[1,c(x,y)].$

Moreover, if (4.45) is valid, then $\mathscr{K}_h[u]$ can be selected as follows:

(4.46) $h^{-2}[-2(1 + c)u_0 + u_1 + cu_2 + u_3 + cu_4]$,   if $b(x,y) = 0$

(4.47) $h^{-2}[-2(c + 1 - b)u_0 + (1 - b)u_1 + (c - b)u_2 + (1 - b)u_3$
$$+ (c - b)u_4 + bu_5 + bu_7],\quad \text{if } b(x,y) > 0$$

(4.48) $h^{-2}[-2(c + 1 + b)u_0 + (b + 1)u_1 + (b + c)u_2 + (b + 1)u_3$
$$+ (b + c)u_4 - bu_6 - bu_8],\quad \text{if } b(x,y) < 0.$$

Proof:

Consider first the sufficiency. Suppose (4.45) is valid. If $b(x,y) = 0$, then $\alpha_6 = \alpha_7 = \alpha_8 = 0$ satisfy (4.39)–(4.44). Then (4.33)–(4.38) imply $\alpha_0 = -2 - 2c$, $\alpha_1 = \alpha_3 = 1$, $\alpha_2 = \alpha_4 = c$, $\alpha_5 = 0$, from which (4.46) follows. If $b(x,y) > 0$, then $\alpha_6 = \alpha_8 = 0$ and $\alpha_7 = b$ satisfy (4.39)–(4.44). Then (4.33)–(4.38) imply $\alpha_0 = -2 - 2c + 2b$, $\alpha_1 = \alpha_3 = 1 - b$, $\alpha_2 = \alpha_4 = c - b$, $\alpha_5 = b$, and (4.47) follows. Finally, assume $b(x,y) < 0$. Then $\alpha_6 = \alpha_8 = -b$ and $\alpha_7 = 0$ satisfy (4.39)–(4.44). From (4.33)–(4.38), $\alpha_0 = -2 - 2c - 2b$, $\alpha_1 = \alpha_3 = 1 + b$, $\alpha_2 = \alpha_4 = c + b$, $\alpha_5 = 0$, and (4.48) follows, thus completing the proof of the sufficiency.

Consider next the necessity. It will be shown that the assumption

(4.49) $|b(x,y)| \geq \min [1, c(x,y)]$

leads, in each possible case, to a contradiction.

Case 1. If $b(x,y) > 0$ and $\min [1, c(x,y)] = c$, then (4.14), (4.41) and (4.49) imply $2\alpha_6 - \alpha_7 + \alpha_8 < c - 2b \leq -c$. Thus $\alpha_7 > c$. But (4.21) and (4.43) imply $\alpha_7 < c$, which is a contradiction.

Case 2. If $b > 0$ and $\min [1, c] = 1$, the proof is analogous to Case 1.

Case 3. If $b < 0$ and $\min [1, c] = 1$, then (4.44) and (4.49) imply $\alpha_6 - \alpha_7 + \alpha_8 \geq 2$, from which it follows that $\alpha_6 + \alpha_8 \geq 2$. But (4.21) and (4.42) imply $\alpha_6 < 1$, so that $\alpha_8 > 1$. However, (4.40) and (4.44) imply $\alpha_8 < 1$, which is a contradiction.

Case 4. If $b < 0$ and $\min [1, c] = c$, the proof is analogous to Case 3.

Thus, by contradiction, the necessity follows easily and the theorem is proved.

The fundamental numerical importance of Theorem 4.2 is that condition (4.45) is practical and easy to apply and that when it is satisfied a $\mathscr{K}_h$ is given explicitly by (4.46)–(4.48). However, the incorporation of

(4.40)–(4.48) into a numerical method, because of the point arrangement involved, requires in general a modification like that given in Greenspan [2].

EXERCISES

1. Determine constants w_1, w_2, w_3, w_4 such that under the transformation

$$x = w_1 x^* + w_2 y^*,$$
$$y = w_3 x^* + w_4 y^*,$$

the equation $u_{xx} + u_{xy} - 2u_{yy} = 0$ transforms into an equation which has no $u_{x^*y^*}$ term. Show that the resulting partial differential equation is also elliptic on E^2.

2. Find a five-point difference analogue at (x,y) for each of the following elliptic equations and determine an upper bound for h so that the α_i satisfy the conditions of Lemma 2.1.

(a) $u_{xx} + u_{yy} + u_y = 0$.

(b) $u_{xx} + u_{yy} + 3u_x - 2u_y = 0$.

(c) $u_{xx} + u_{yy} + 3u_x - 2u_y = 1$.

(d) $u_{xx} + u_{yy} - 3u_x + 4u_y - 7u = e^{xy}$.

(e) $3u_{xx} + u_{yy} = 0$.

(f) $3u_{xx} + u_{yy} - u = 0$.

(g) $4u_{xx} + 5u_{yy} - 6u_y + 8u_x - 9u = e^{-xy}$.

3. Let R be a simply connected bounded region whose boundary S is a contour. Let $\phi(x,y)$ be continuous on S and let $W(x,y)$ be continuous on $R \cup S$. The Poisson Problem is that of finding a function $u(x,y)$ that has the properties

(a) $\Delta u \equiv W(x,y)$,   on R

(b) $u \equiv \phi$,   on S

(c) $u \in C(R \cup S)$,

(d) $u \in C^2(R)$.

It is known that the Poisson Problem has a unique solution (see, e.g., Courant and Hilbert [1]).

Consider the following numerical method for approximating the solution of the Poisson Problem: Apply Method D of Chapter 2 but replace the 0 on the right hand side of (2.9) with $W(x,y)$.

Show that the above numerical method has a unique solution and that if $u \in C^2(R \cup S)$ then the numerical solution converges to the analytical solution as h converges to zero.

4. Let R be the interior of the unit circle S. Let S^* be those points of S for which $y \leq 0$ so that S' is that set of points of S for which $y > 0$. Extend Methods M_1 and M_2, and for $(\bar{x},\bar{y}) = (0,0)$ and $h = .25$, approximate the function u which

(a) satisfies $u_{xx} + 2u_{yy} = -6x$, on R,

(b) is identical with $x^3 - 3xy^2$ on S^*,

(c) satisfies $\dfrac{\partial u}{\partial n} = 3x^3 - 9xy^2$ on S',

(d) has continuous second partials on R, and

(e) is continuous on $R \cup S$.

Compare your results with the exact solution $u = x^3 - 3xy^2$.

5. Let S be the square with vertices $(0,0)$, $(1,0)$, $(1,1)$, and $(0,1)$, and let R be the interior of S. On $G = R \cup S$ consider a Dirichlet type problem for $4u_{xx} + x^2 u_{xy} + 4u_{yy} = 0$ with $f = x^2 - y^2$ on S. For $(\bar{x},\bar{y}) = (0,0)$ and $h = .25$, find an approximate solution to the given problem and compare your results with the exact solution $u = x^2 - y^2$.

6. Motivate (4.45) as follows. Show first that (4.20), (4.34)–(4.38), and the assumptions $\alpha_1 = \alpha_3$, $\alpha_2 = \alpha_4$, $\alpha_5 = \alpha_7$, $\alpha_6 = \alpha_8$ imply both
$$b < 1 - 2\alpha_6, \quad b < c - 2\alpha_6.$$
From these latter inequalities, show then that at best
$$b < \min [1,c].$$

7. (a) Show that $|b(x,y)| \leq \min [1,c(x,y)]$ is both necessary and sufficient for the existence of a $\mathcal{K}_h$ which satisfies (4.19) and (in place of (4.20)–(4.22))

(4.20′) $\qquad\qquad \alpha_0 < 0, \quad \alpha_i \geq 0, \quad i = 1, 2, \cdots, 8,$

(4.21′) $\qquad\qquad\qquad \sum_1^8 \alpha_i > 0,$

(4.22′) $\qquad\qquad\qquad \sum_0^8 \alpha_i = 0.$

(b) If $|b(x,y)| \leq \min [1,c(x,y)]$, produce a $\mathcal{K}_h$ which satisfies (4.19) and (4.20′)–(4.22′).

8. Show that the result of making h small in (4.6) is to negate the effect of the u_x, u_y, and u terms in (4.5). Thus show that the assumption for (4.18) that the α_i be independent of h is realistic.

9. Show that the α_i, $i = 0, 1, 2, 3, 4$, given by (4.6), with h given by (4.10), will satisfy the assumptions of the Star Lemma iff $F \equiv 0$.

10. Show that the $\mathcal{K}_h$ given in (4.47) is not unique.

11. Is Theorem 4.2 still valid if $\mathcal{K}_h$ is restricted to functions u which not only are of class $C^2(R)$ but which in addition satisfy the equation $\mathcal{K}[u] = 0$?

12. Justify whether or not the simplex method of linear programming can be applied to solve (4.39)–(4.44).

13. Find a simply connected region R and a solution $u(x,y)$ of the elliptic equation $u_{xx} + u_{yy} + u = 0$ on R such that u is continuous on $R \cup S$ but does *not* attain its maximum value on S.

14. Formulate a definition of a "best" five-point difference analogue of the Laplace equation (see, e.g., Greenspan [4]). Construct then a "best" analogue and discuss whether or not it is unique.

15. Show that condition (4.45) can be eliminated from Theorem 4.2 if one introduces a rectangular (see Exercise 8, Chapter 2) grid.

CHAPTER 5

THREE DIMENSIONAL PROBLEMS WITH AXIAL SYMMETRY

5.1. INTRODUCTION

Of fundamental interest in the applied sciences are problems whose mathematical formulation requires at least three dimensions. However, since two dimensional problems are, in many cases, easier to handle than three dimensional ones, the mathematical literature is surfeited with attempts to reduce more general problems to ones in two dimensions, and under the assumption that a three dimensional problem has a solution which is symmetrical about an axis, which is often the case, such an approach is valid.

Of particular interest in such diverse fields as electrostatic field theory, heat and ideal fluid flow, and stress concentration theory (see, e.g., Shortley, Weller, Darby, and Gamble [1], Weinstein [1]) are problems that reduce, under the assumption of axial symmetry, to the study on a bounded, simply connected region R of the elliptic differential equation

$$(5.1) \qquad u_{xx} + u_{yy} + \frac{K}{y} u_y = 0,$$

where K is an arbitrary, but fixed, real constant. In operator notation, (5.1) will be written

$$(5.1') \qquad L_K[u] = 0,$$

71

where linear operator L_K is defined by

$$(5.2) \qquad L_K \equiv \frac{\partial^2}{\partial x^2} + \frac{\partial^2}{\partial y^2} + \frac{K}{y}\frac{\partial}{\partial y}.$$

Now, up to the present, all the problems considered in this book were related to equations whose coefficients, though not necessarily constant, were both *continuous* and *bounded* on a given region R. Existence and uniqueness for such linear problems have been explored extensively from the theoretical point of view (see, e.g., Courant and Hilbert [1], Miranda [3]), and if R is bounded away from the x-axis, then (5.1) falls into this category. For such an R the numerical treatment is a straightforward extension of the previous methods. However, the physically significant problems relative to (5.1) require that the boundary S of R contain a nondegenerate portion of the x-axis, so that, for $K \neq 0$, the coefficient $\dfrac{K}{y}$ of u_y in (5.2) is *unbounded*. Boundary problems for such S have not been studied until very recently (see, e.g., Huber [1,2], M. Schechter [1], Warten [1], Greenspan and Warten [1]), and it is with the numerical treatment of such problems that this chapter is concerned.

5.2. ANALYTICAL BACKGROUND

In the Euclidean plane E^2, E_0 will represent the open, upper-half plane and R will represent a nonempty, open, simply connected, bounded subset of E_0. With respect to the boundary S of R, it will be assumed that $S = \bar{S}_{(1)} \cup S_{(2)}$, where $\bar{S}_{(1)} \cap S_{(2)} = \emptyset$, $\bar{S}_{(1)}$ is a closed nondegenerate interval on the x-axis whose interior is $S_{(1)}$, and $S_{(2)}$ is contained in E_0. If the end points of $\bar{S}_{(1)}$ have abscissas x_1 and x_2, then it will be assumed that any vertical line which does not pass through $(x_1,0)$ or $(x_2,0)$ meets $S_{(2)}$ in at most one point. Also, recall that, as usual, $G = R \cup S$.

One says that u satisfies a Hölder condition with exponent α on a set X iff there exist constants H and α, $0 < \alpha < 1$, such that if P,Q are arbitrary points of X then

$$|u(P) - u(Q)| \leq H\,|P - Q|^\alpha.$$

Note, of course, that if u satisfies a Hölder condition on set X, then it is uniformly continuous on X.

Of interest will be the classes $C^{2+\alpha}(G)$ and $C^{2+\alpha}(R)$, $0 < \alpha < 1$, where $C^{2+\alpha}(G)$ is the class of functions $u \in C^2(G)$ whose second order partials are Hölder continuous with exponent α on G and $C^{2+\alpha}(R)$ is the class of functions $u \in C^2(R)$ whose second order partials are Hölder continuous with exponent α on every closed and bounded subset of R.

Definition 5.1

A region $R \subset E^2$ is said to be of class $C^{2+\alpha}$ iff every boundary point $Q \in S$ satisfies the following condition: If Q is taken as the origin, the coordinate axes may be so chosen that the x-axis is tangent to S at Q and there is a circular neighborhood of Q in which S is representable in the form $y = f(x)$, where f is single valued and twice Hölder continuously differentiable with exponent α.

Definition 5.2

A bounded region $R \subset E_0$ is said to be of class S_α iff

(a) S is a simple closed curve which is composed of a finite number of arcs, each of class $C^{2+\alpha}$,
(b) $S \cap (x\text{-axis})$ is a nonempty, closed, nondegenerate interval, and
(c) at each corner point $Q \in S$, there is a closed circular disc (of positive radius) which has only Q in common with $R \cup S$.

It follows readily that rectangular and circular regions, for example, are of class S_α.

The following existence theorems are now given.

Theorem 5.1

Let $K < 1$ and let region R be of class S_α. If $\phi(x,y) \in C(S)$, then there exists a unique function $u(x,y)$ such that

(5.3) $$L_K(u) \equiv 0, \quad \text{on } R$$

(5.4) $$u \equiv \phi, \quad \text{on } S, \text{ and}$$

(5.5) $$u \in [C(G) \cap C^2(R)].$$

For the proof, see M. Schechter [1] and Greenspan and Warten [1].

Theorem 5.2

Let $K \geq 1$ and let region R be of class S_α. If $\phi(x,y)$ is bounded and continuous on $S_{(2)}$, then there is a unique function u such that

(5.6) $\qquad\qquad L_K(u) \equiv 0, \qquad$ on R

(5.7) $\qquad\qquad u \equiv \phi, \qquad$ on $S_{(2)}$

(5.8) $\qquad\qquad u \in [C(G \cap E_0) \cap C^2(R)]$, and

(5.9) $\qquad\qquad u$ is bounded on R.

Moreover, u can be continued analytically across S_1.

For the proof, see Huber [2], M. Schechter [1], and Warten [1].

In view of Theorems 5.1 and 5.2, we are assured that the following problems, with which we shall be concerned, have unique solutions.

Problem D$_1$

Let $K < 1$ and let R be of class S_α. If $\phi(x,y) \in C(S)$, find $u(x,y)$ that satisfies (5.3)–(5.5).

Problem D$_2$

Let $K \geq 1$ and let R be of class S_α. If $\phi(x,y)$ is bounded and continuous on $S_{(2)}$ find $u(x,y)$ that satisfies (5.6)–(5.9).

To produce solutions of Problems D_1 and D_2 is exceedingly difficult and for this reason we proceed to discuss very accurate methods of approximation. Fundamental to each method will be the replacement of R by a region R_σ on which the coefficient of u_y in (1.1) is bounded. This is accomplished as follows. Fix $\sigma > 0$ and let the line $y = \sigma$ intersect S in (a,σ) and (b,σ) where $a < b$ and the straight line segment joining (a,σ) and (b,σ) is contained in $\bar{R}$ (see Figure 5.1). If E_σ is the set of all points (x,y) for which $y > \sigma$, then define $R_\sigma = R \cap E_\sigma$. Let S_σ be the boundary of R_σ, and set $G_\sigma = R_\sigma \cup S_\sigma$.

Now, fix any point $(\bar{x},\bar{y})$ on the line $y = \sigma$ and for a fixed, positive constant h, determine the planar grid points $(\bar{x} + ph, \bar{y} + qh)$, $p = 0, \pm 1, \pm 2, \cdots$; $q = 0, \pm 1, \pm 2, \cdots$. The set of all horizontal and all vertical lines through the grid points is, of course, a planar lattice. The set of all points of intersection of the planar lattice with S_σ is called the set of boundary lattice points and is denoted by $S_{\sigma,h}$. The set of all planar grid points that are elements of R_σ is called the set of interior lattice points and

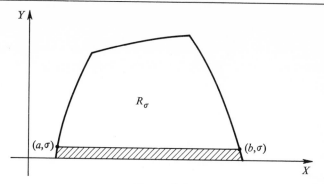

Figure 5.1

is denoted by $R_{\sigma,h}$. Also, set $G_{\sigma,h} = R_{\sigma,h} \cup S_{\sigma,h}$. Let $R_{\sigma,h}$ contain m points that are numbered in a one-to-one fashion with the integers $1, 2, \cdots, m$ in the fashion described in Step 2, Method D, Section 2.3.

5.3. DERIVATION OF THE DIFFERENCE EQUATION APPROXIMATIONS

Using the notation of the point pattern in Figure 2.1, set

$$(5.10) \qquad u_{xx} + u_{yy} + \frac{K}{y} u_y \equiv \sum_0^4 \alpha_i u_i,$$

where the α_i are to be determined and the left-hand expression in (5.10) is to be considered at the point numbered 0. Substitution of finite Taylor expansions about (x,y) for u_1, u_2, u_3, u_4 implies

$$(5.11) \quad u_0(\alpha_0 + \alpha_1 + \alpha_2 + \alpha_3 + \alpha_4) + u_x(h_1\alpha_1 - h_3\alpha_3) + u_y(h_2\alpha_2 - h_4\alpha_4)$$

$$+ \frac{\alpha_1 h_1^2}{2} u_{xx}(\xi_1, y) + \frac{\alpha_2 h_2^2}{2} u_{yy}(x, \xi_2) + \frac{\alpha_3 h_3^2}{2} u_{xx}(\xi_3, y) + \frac{\alpha_4 h_4^2}{2} u_{yy}(x, \xi_4)$$

$$\equiv u_{xx} + u_{yy} + \frac{K}{y} u_y,$$

where $x < x + \xi_1 < x + h_1$, $x - h_3 < x - \xi_3 < x$, $y < y + \xi_2 < y + h_2$, $y - h_4 < y - \xi_4 < y$. By the continuity of u_{xx} and u_{yy}, one has then from (5.11) that

$$(5.12) \quad u_0(\alpha_0 + \alpha_1 + \alpha_2 + \alpha_3 + \alpha_4) + u_x(h_1\alpha_1 - h_3\alpha_3) + u_y(h_2\alpha_2 - h_4\alpha_4)$$

$$+ u_{xx}\left(\frac{\alpha_1 h_1^2}{2} + \frac{\alpha_3 h_3^2}{2}\right) + u_{yy}\left(\frac{\alpha_2 h_2^2}{2} + \frac{\alpha_4 h_4^2}{2}\right)$$

$$+ \sum_1^4 \frac{\epsilon_i \alpha_i h_i^2}{2} \equiv u_{xx} + u_{yy} + \frac{K}{y} u_y,$$

where $\epsilon_i \to 0$ as $h \to 0$. Setting the coefficients of u_0, u_x, u_y, u_{xx}, and u_{yy} on the left side of (5.12) equal to the corresponding coefficients on the right side yields

$$\alpha_0 + \alpha_1 + \alpha_2 + \alpha_3 + \alpha_4 = 0,$$

$$h_1\alpha_1 - h_3\alpha_3 = 0,$$

$$(5.13) \qquad\qquad h_2\alpha_2 - h_4\alpha_4 = \frac{K}{y},$$

$$\alpha_1 h_1^2 + \alpha_3 h_3^2 = 2,$$

$$\alpha_2 h_2^2 + \alpha_4 h_4^2 = 2,$$

the solution of which is

$$(5.14) \quad \alpha_0 = -\left[\frac{2}{h_1 h_3} + \frac{2}{h_2 h_4} + \frac{K(h_4 - h_2)}{y h_2 h_4}\right], \quad \alpha_1 = \frac{2}{h_1(h_1 + h_3)},$$

$$\alpha_2 = \frac{2y + h_4 K}{y h_2(h_2 + h_4)}, \quad \alpha_3 = \frac{2}{h_3(h_1 + h_3)}, \quad \alpha_4 = \frac{2y - h_2 K}{y h_4(h_2 + h_4)}.$$

One is then motivated to select as an approximation of (5.1) the difference equation

(5.15)

$$-\left[\frac{2}{h_1 h_3} + \frac{2}{h_2 h_4} + \frac{K(h_4 - h_2)}{y h_2 h_4}\right] u_0 + \frac{2}{h_1(h_1 + h_3)} u_1 + \frac{2y + h_4 K}{y h_2(h_2 + h_4)} u_2$$

$$+ \frac{2}{h_3(h_1 + h_3)} u_3 + \frac{2y - h_2 K}{y h_4(h_2 + h_4)} u_4 = 0.$$

Note that since, by assumption, a vertical line can intersect S_2 in at most one point, one must have $h_4 \leq h_2$ at each point of $R_{o,h}$. Also, note that since $y \geq \sigma$ at each point of $G_{o,h}$, then the condition

$$(5.16) \qquad\qquad |K| h < 2\sigma$$

implies that the α_i of (5.14) satisfy the assumptions of Lemma 2.2, the Star Lemma.

Motivated next by Theorem 5.2, consider a point $(x,y) \in S_{h,\sigma}$ which lies on the line $y = \sigma$ but is not (a,σ) or (b,σ). Let the closest points of G_h to (x,y) in the east, north, and west directions be $(x + h_1, y)$, $(x, y + h)$, $(x - h_3, y)$, respectively, and let (x,y), $(x + h_1, y)$, $(x, y + h)$, $(x - h_3, y)$ be numbered 0, 1, 2, 3, respectively, as in Figure 5.2. Note immediately the additional restrictive assumption that the y coordinate of the point

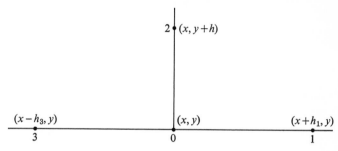

Figure 5.2

numbered 2 be $y + h$, where h is the grid constant. The reason for this assumption will become apparent shortly, but it should be remarked that for a large variety of boundaries like rectangles, quarter circles, and quarter ellipses, the condition is satisfied at each $(x,\sigma) \in S_{h,\sigma}$ for an appropriately selected $(\bar{x},\bar{y})$ and for all sufficiently small h. It will be understood throughout the remainder of the discussion that this assumption has been made.

For $K \geq 1$, consider at the point $(x,\sigma) = (x,y)$ displayed in Figure 5.2

(5.17)
$$u_{xx} + u_{yy} + \frac{K}{y} u_y \equiv \sum_0^3 \alpha_i u_i.$$

Substitution of Taylor expansions into (5.17) implies

$$u_0(\alpha_0 + \alpha_1 + \alpha_2 + \alpha_3) + u_x(\alpha_1 h_1 - \alpha_3 h_3) + \alpha_2 h u_y$$

$$+ \frac{u_{xx}}{2}(h_1^2 \alpha_1 + h_3^2 \alpha_3) + \frac{h^2 \alpha_2}{2} u_{yy} + \sum_1^3 [O(\alpha_i h_i^3)]$$

$$\equiv u_{xx} + u_{yy} + \frac{K}{y} u_y, \qquad 0 < h_i \leq h.$$

Setting corresponding coefficients of u_0, u_x, u_y, u_{xx}, and u_{yy} equal, and noting that $y = \sigma$, implies

$$\alpha_0 + \alpha_1 + \alpha_2 + \alpha_3 = 0,$$

$$\alpha_1 h_1 - \alpha_3 h_3 = 0,$$

(5.18) $$\alpha_2 h = \frac{K}{\sigma},$$

$$h_1^2 \alpha_1 + h_3^2 \alpha_3 = 2,$$

$$h^2 \alpha_2 = 2.$$

Now, if one selects

(5.19) $$h = \frac{2\sigma}{K},$$

then the unique solution of (5.18) is

$$\alpha_0 = -\frac{2}{h^2} - \frac{2}{h_1(h_1 + h_3)} - \frac{2}{h_3(h_1 + h_3)},$$

(5.20)

$$\alpha_1 = \frac{2}{h_1(h_1 + h_3)}, \quad \alpha_2 = \frac{2}{h^2}, \quad \alpha_3 = \frac{2}{h_3(h_1 + h_3)},$$

and a difference equation approximation is

$$\left[-\frac{2}{h^2} - \frac{2}{h_1(h_1 + h_3)} - \frac{2}{h_3(h_1 + h_3)} \right] u_0$$

(5.21)

$$+ \frac{2}{h_1(h_1 + h_3)} u_1 + \frac{2}{h^2} u_2 + \frac{2}{h_3(h_1 + h_3)} u_3 = 0.$$

Note that the α_i in (5.20) again satisfy the conditions of Lemma 2.2 and that if one had not assumed the coordinates of the point numbered 2 in Figure 5.2 to be $(x, y + h)$, then (5.18) need not have had any solution at all.

5.4. THE NUMERICAL METHODS

The numerical methods are now described as follows.

Method D_1

To approximate the solution of Problem D_1, proceed as follows.

Step 1. Determine h and σ to satisfy (5.16). For fixed $(\bar{x},\bar{y})$ on the line $y = \sigma$, construct $R_{\sigma,h}$ and $S_{\sigma,h}$. Number the points of $R_{\sigma,h}$ as indicated in Section 5.2. If $S_{\sigma,h}$ contains n points, number these in a one-to-one fashion with the integers $m + 1, \cdots, m + n$.

Step 2. If $(x,y) \in S_{\sigma,h}$ and is numbered 0, and if $y = \sigma$ and $x = a$ or b, then set $U_0 = \phi(x,y)$.

Step 3. If $(x,y) \in S_{\sigma,h}$ and is numbered 0, and if $y \neq \sigma$, set $U_0 = \phi(x,y)$.

Step 4. If $(x,y) \in S_{\sigma,h}$ and is numbered 0, and if $y = \sigma$ but $x \neq a$, $x \neq b$, then set $U_0 = \phi(x,0)$.

Step 5. If $(x,y) \in R_{\sigma,h}$ and is numbered zero, and if its four neighbors in $G_{\sigma,h}$ are numbered 1–4 as in Figure 2.1, then write down, in subscript notation, the difference equation

$$
(5.22) \quad
\begin{aligned}
&-\left[\frac{2}{h_1 h_3} + \frac{2}{h_2 h_4} + \frac{K(h_4 - h_2)}{y h_2 h_4}\right] U_0 + \frac{2}{h_1(h_1 + h_3)} U_1 \\
&+ \frac{2y + h_4 K}{y h_2(h_2 + h_4)} U_2 + \frac{2}{h_3(h_1 + h_3)} U_3 + \frac{2y - h_2 K}{y h_4(h_2 + h_4)} U_4 = 0.
\end{aligned}
$$

Do this in consecutive fashion at the points numbered $1, 2, \cdots, m$.

Step 6. If the results of Steps 1–4 are substituted into the linear algebraic system generated in Step 5, there result m linear algebraic equations in $U_1, U_2, \cdots, U_m$. Solve this system.

Step 7. Let the results of Steps 1–4 and 6 represent the approximate solution on $G_{\sigma,h}$ of Problem D_1.

Method D_2

To approximate the solution of Problem D_2, proceed as follows.

Step 1. Determine h and σ to satisfy (5.19). For fixed $(\bar{x},\bar{y})$ on the line $y = \sigma$, construct $R_{\sigma,h}$ and $S_{\sigma,h}$. Denote by $S_{\sigma,h}^*$ those points of $S_{\sigma,h}$ which lie on the line $y = \sigma$ and are not (a,σ) or (b,σ). Let $R_{\sigma,h} \cup S_{\sigma,h}^*$ contain m' points and number these in a one-to-one fashion with the integers $1 - m'$ so that the numbers are increasing in each row from left to right and in each column from bottom to top. If $S_{\sigma,h} - S_{\sigma,h}^*$ contains n' points, number these in a one-to-one fashion with the integers $m' + 1, m' + 2, \cdots, m' + n'$.

Step 2. If $(x,y) \in [S_{\sigma,h} - S_{\sigma,h}^*]$ and is numbered 0, set $U_0 = \phi(x,y)$.

Step 3. If $(x,y) \in S^*_{\sigma,h}$ and is numbered 0 as in Figure 5.2, write down in subscript notation

(5.23)
$$\left[-\frac{2}{h^2} - \frac{2}{h_1(h_1 + h_3)} - \frac{2}{h_3(h_1 + h_3)} \right] U_0$$
$$+ \frac{2}{h_1(h_1 + h_3)} U_1 + \frac{2}{h^2} U_2 + \frac{2}{h_3(h_1 + h_3)} U_3 = 0.$$

Step 4. If $(x,y) \in R_{\sigma,h}$ and is numbered 0 as in Figure 2.1, write down in subscript notation, difference equation (5.22).

Step 5. If the results of Step 2 are substituted in the linear algebraic system generated by Steps 3 and 4, there result m' equations in U_1, $U_2, \cdots, U_{m'}$. Solve this system.

Step 6. Let the results of Steps 2 and 5 represent the approximate solution on $G_{\sigma,h}$ of Problem D_2.

The uniqueness of the solution of the algebraic equations for Methods D_1 and D_2 is a consequence of Lemma 2.2 and, hence, of a strong max–min property, while the convergence to solutions of class $C^2(G)$ as $\sigma \to 0$ for $K \neq 0$, and as $\sigma^2 + h^2 \to 0$ for $K = 0$, follows in a fashion completely analogous to that described in Section 2.5 (consult, e.g., Greenspan and Warten [1]).

Note that difference approximations more complicated than (5.15) and (5.21) were derived by Warten [1] and more complicated, but higher order, ones were given by Davidenko [4]. Also note that existence and uniqueness of solutions of boundary value problems for (5.1) have been explored by others (consult references (57)–(62) in Weinstein [2]).

5.5. EXAMPLES

A number of examples were run on the CDC 1604 and the two described next are typical.

Example 1. Let region R be the circular sector in the first quadrant bounded by the curves whose equations are $x^2 + y^2 = 1$, $x = 0$ and $y = 0$. Consider Problem D_1 with $K = -5$, $\phi = x + y^6$. Method D_1 was applied with $\sigma = .06$, $(\bar{x}, \bar{y}) = (0, .06)$, $h = .02$. The resulting set of 1760 linear algebraic equations was solved by over-relaxation with $\omega = 1.8$ and zero initial vector. The running time was 4 minutes. Selected, but typical, results are recorded under U in Table 5.1.

TABLE 5.1

x	y	U	Exact Solution $u = x + y^6$
.98	.08	.98000	.98000
.26	.10	.26000	.26000
.38	.12	.38000	.38000
.70	.12	.70000	.70000
.52	.16	.52001	.52002
.48	.18	.40003	.40003
.66	.20	.66006	.66006
.86	.22	.86011	.86011
.10	.26	.10030	.10031
.74	.26	.74030	.74031
.02	.30	.02072	.02073
.26	.32	.26105	.26107
.32	.34	.32151	.32154
.68	.36	.68214	.68217
.50	.38	.50296	.50301
.38	.42	.38541	.38548
.08	.44	.08721	.08726
.76	.46	.76942	.76947
.18	.48	.19213	.19223
.40	.50	.41549	.41562
.82	.52	.83974	.83977
.28	.56	.31066	.31084
.06	.60	.10657	.10665
.50	.64	.56850	.56871
.30	.70	.41735	.41764
.68	.72	.81928	.81931
.14	.80	.40188	.40214
.36	.84	.71104	.71130
.20	.90	.73120	.73144
.38	.92	.98631	.98635
.34	.94	1.02987	1.02986
.16	.98	1.04577	1.04584

Example 2. Let R be a rectangular region whose boundary has consecutive vertices $A(0,0)$, $B(1,0)$, $C(1,2)$, and $D(0,2)$. Consider Problem D_2 with $K = 1$, $\phi = -2x^2 + y^2$. Method D_2 was applied with $\sigma = .02$, $(\bar{x},\bar{y}) = (0, .02)$, $h = .04$. The resulting set of 1200 linear algebraic equations was solved by over-relaxation with $\omega = 1.8$ and zero initial vector. The running

time was 3 minutes. The numerical solution agreed with the analytical solution $u = -2x^2 + y^2$ to at least eight decimal places.

It should also be noted that Methods D_1 and D_2 yielded good approximations to certain problems in which u_y or u_{yy} become infinite as y approaches zero.

EXERCISES

1. (a) Show that any rectangular shaped region R is of class S_α.

   (b) Show that any circular shaped region R is of class S_α.

2. (Correspondence Principle of A. Weinstein.) Let region R be of class S_α. Show that if u is a solution on R of $L_K[u] = 0$, then $v = y^{K-1}u$ is a solution on R of $L_{2-K}[v] = 0$. Conversely, show that if v is a solution on R of $L_{2-K}[v] = 0$, then $u = y^{1-K}v$ is a solution on R of $L_K[u] = 0$.

3. Let R be that portion of the interior of the unit circle which is contained in the first quadrant. Consider Problem D_1 with $K = -5$, $\phi = x + y^6$.

(a) Select an appropriate $(\bar{x}, \bar{y})$ and h and apply Method D_1 with

   (i) $\sigma = .5$.   (iii) $\sigma = .1$.
   (ii) $\sigma = .3$.   (iv) $\sigma = .01$.

(b) Compare the approximate results obtained in part (a) with the exact solution $u = x + y^6$.

4. Let S be the rectangle with vertices $(0,0)$, $(1,0)$, $(1,2)$, and $(0,2)$, and let R be the interior of S. Consider Problem D_1 with $K = -1$, $\phi = x - y^2$.

(a) Select an appropriate $(\bar{x}, \bar{y})$ and h, and apply Method D_1 with

   (i) $\sigma = .5$.   (iii) $\sigma = .1$.
   (ii) $\sigma = .3$.   (iv) $\sigma = .01$.

(b) Compare the approximate results obtained in part (a) with the exact solution $u = x - y^2$.

5. Let R be defined as in Exercise 3. Consider Problem D_2 with $K = 1$, $\phi = -2x^2 + y^2$.

(a) Select an appropriate $(\bar{x}, \bar{y})$ and apply Method D_2 with

   (i) $\sigma = .5$.   (iii) $\sigma = .1$.
   (ii) $\sigma = .3$.   (iv) $\sigma = .01$.

(b) Compare the approximate results obtained in part (a) with the exact solution $u = -2x^2 + y^2$.

6. Let R be defined as in Exercise 4. Consider Problem D_2 with $K = 2$, $\phi = -3x^2 + y^2$.

(a) Select an appropriate $(\bar{x}, \bar{y})$ and apply Method D_2 with

(i) $\sigma = .5$.   (iii) $\sigma = .1$.

(ii) $\sigma = .3$.   (iv) $\sigma = .01$.

(b) Compare the approximate results obtained in part (a) with the exact solution $u = -3x^2 + y^2$.

7. Let R be the region given in Exercise 4. Consider Problem D_1 with $K = \frac{1}{2}$, $\phi = x + y^{1/2}$.

(a) For $(\bar{x}, \bar{y}) = (0,0)$ and an appropriate h, apply Method D_1 with

(i) $\sigma = .5$.   (iii) $\sigma = .1$.

(ii) $\sigma = .3$.   (iv) $\sigma = .01$.

(b) Compare the approximate results obtained in part (a) with the exact solution $u = x + y^{1/2}$.

(c) What inferences can you make with regard to Method D_1 from this particular example since $u \notin C^2(R \cup S)$?

8. Is it possible to approximate the solution of Problem D_1 by applying the Correspondence Principle (see Exercise 2) and Method D_2?

9. Consider the region R of Exercise 4. On the segment joining $(0,0)$ and $(1,0)$ define $\phi(x,y) = -2x$. On the remainder of S define $\phi(x,y) = -2x^2 + y^2$.

(a) Show that there does not exist a function $u(x,y)$ which is bounded on R and satisfies

(i) $u_{xx} + u_{yy} + \dfrac{1}{y} u_y = 0$,   on R

(ii) $u \equiv \phi$,   on S, and

(iii) $u \in [C(R \cup S) \cap C^2(R)]$.

(b) For $(\bar{x}, \bar{y}) = (0,0)$, $\sigma = .1$ and $h = .1$, show that setting $U(x,.1) = \phi(x,0)$ and applying (5.22) at each point of R_h yields a system of algebraic equations whose solution exists and is unique.

(c) In view of part (a), what value can be ascribed to the numbers generated in part (b)?

10. Show that a numerical solution generated by Method D_1 or Method D_2 always possesses a strong max–min property on $G_{\sigma,h}$.

CHAPTER 6

LINEAR ELLIPTIC PROBLEMS IN THREE AND MORE DIMENSIONS

6.1. INTRODUCTION

Numerically, the extension to three or more dimensions of the methods described in Chapters 2–5 is a straightforward process, prototype problems of which will be examined in this chapter. Analytically, however, existence and uniqueness theorems do not extend easily. Even the two dimensional Dirichlet Problem does not extend directly as a well posed problem in three dimensions unless some further qualification, like a cone condition, is imposed on the boundary surface S (see, e.g., Courant and Hilbert [1], Petrovsky [2]). Moreover, the modern approach to existence and uniqueness by means of generalized solutions (see, e.g., Visik and Ladyzenskaya [1]) is of little use if one is interested in pointwise numerical convergence, unless some means, like the Lemma of Sobolev (see, e.g., Nirenberg [2], p. 30), is available to connect convergence in an L_p norm to convergence in the sup norm. It should be clear then that many analytical questions are still undecided and that much research is still in progress.

6.2. THE DIRICHLET PROBLEM

If to each point P of a set $M \subset E^3$ there corresponds by some transformation f a unique point Q of a set $N \subset E^3$, f is said to map M **into** N. If to each point $Q \in N$ there is some point $P \in M$ such that $f(P) = Q, f$ is

84

said to map M **onto** N. If f maps M onto N and if to each point $Q \in N$ there exists a unique point P such that $f(P) = Q$, f is said to be one-to-one and the indicated transformation from N to M is denoted by f^{-1}. If f is one-to-one and both f and f^{-1} are continuous, f is said to be a *homeomorphism* and M and N are said to be *homeomorphic*.

Let R be a three dimensional bounded region homeomorphic to the interior of the unit sphere, i.e., to the point set in E^3 whose coordinates satisfy the inequality $x^2 + y^2 + z^2 < 1$. Let S be the boundary of R and set $G = R \cup S$. Then if $\phi(x,y,z) \in C(S)$, the Dirichlet Problem to be considered is that of finding a function $u(x,y,z) \in C^2(R)$ that satisfies the following three conditions:

(a) u is a solution on R of

(6.1) $$u_{xx} + u_{yy} + u_{zz} = 0,$$

(b) $u \equiv \phi$,   on S,

(c) $u \in C(G)$.

Under quite general assumptions on S (see Courant and Hilbert [1], p. 233, p. 372), the above Dirichlet Problem has a unique solution. However, since it is not known in general how to give this solution in closed form, attention will be directed next toward approximating it.

Let $(\bar{x}, \bar{y}, \bar{z})$ be an arbitrary point of G and let h be a positive constant. The set of points $(\bar{x} + ph, \bar{y} + qh, \bar{z} + rh)$, $p = 0, \pm 1, \pm 2, \cdots$; $q = 0, \pm 1, \pm 2, \cdots$; $r = 0, \pm 1, \pm 2, \cdots$, is called a set of grid points. Two grid points are said to be adjacent iff their distance apart is h. The set of all lines, each one of which contains at least one pair of adjacent grid points, is called a lattice. Denote by G_h those points that are *either* grid points in G *or* are points of intersection of S and the lattice. If $(x,y,z) \in [S \cap G_h]$, then (x,y,z) is called a boundary lattice point and the set of all boundary lattice points is denoted by S_h. The set of all points of G_h that are not elements of S_h is called the set of interior lattice points and is denoted by R_h.

If R_h consists of m points we shall number these in a one-to-one fashion with the integers $1, 2, \cdots, m$, while if S_h consists of n points we shall number these in a one-to-one fashion with the integers $m + 1, m + 2, \cdots, m + n$. If $(x,y,z) \in G_h$ and has been numbered t, then $u(x,y,z)$ will be denoted by u_t.

At each point $(x,y,z) \in S_h$, $u(x,y,z) = \phi(x,y,z)$ so that the exact solution is known. At each point $(x,y,z) \in R_h$, let $(x + h_1, y, z)$, $(x - h_2, y, z)$, $(x, y + h_3, z)$, $(x, y - h_4, z)$, $(x, y, z + h_5)$, and $(x, y, z - h_6)$ be those points of G_h that are nearest to (x,y,z) in the positive and negative x, y, and z directions, respectively (see Figure 6.1). Of course $0 < h_i \le h$,

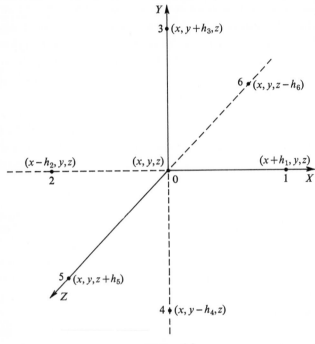

Figure 6.1

$i = 1, 2, \cdots, 6$. If (x,y,z), $(x + h_1, y, z)$, $(x - h_2, y, z)$, $(x, y + h_3, z)$, $(x, y - h_4, z)$, $(x, y, z + h_5)$, and $(x, y, z - h_6)$ are numbered $0, 1, \cdots, 6$, respectively, then write down in proper subscript notation the difference equation

$$(6.2) \quad \left(-\frac{2}{h_1 h_2} - \frac{2}{h_3 h_4} - \frac{2}{h_5 h_6} \right) U_0 + \frac{2}{h_1(h_1 + h_2)} U_1 + \frac{2}{h_2(h_1 + h_2)} U_2$$

$$+ \frac{2}{h_3(h_3 + h_4)} U_3 + \frac{2}{h_4(h_3 + h_4)} U_4 + \frac{2}{h_5(h_5 + h_6)} U_5$$

$$+ \frac{2}{h_6(h_5 + h_6)} U_6 = 0.$$

Application of (6.2) exactly once at each point of R_h and insertion of all the known values of U on S_h yield a system of m linear algebraic equations in $U_1, U_2, \cdots, U_m$, the solution of which, together with the known values of U on S_h, constitute the numerical solution.

It should be noted that the ordering prescribed for the points of R_h in Chapter 2 has not been, though it can be, extended here. That ordering made the linear algebraic system immediately amenable to solution by iteration. One can accomplish the same result in three dimensions merely by ordering the resulting equations with application of (6.2) as follows. For $k = 1, 2, \cdots, m$, let the kth equation be the one which results by applying (6.2) at the point of R_h numbered k.

The derivation of (6.2) is a direct consequence of the same method displayed in Section 2.2. The uniqueness of the solution of the algebraic system and the convergence of the numerical to the analytical solution u when $u \in C^2(G)$ follow in a fashion completely analogous to that described in Chapter 2.

Note also that if an n-dimensional Dirichlet problem were to be considered, all the ideas extend in a natural way, and with regard to the n-dimensional Laplace equation,

$$(6.1')\qquad \frac{\partial^2 u}{\partial x_1^2} + \frac{\partial^2 u}{\partial x_2^2} + \cdots + \frac{\partial^2 u}{\partial x_n^2} = 0,$$

one can readily derive the difference analogue

$$(6.3)\qquad \sum_{i=1}^{n} \left[\frac{-2u_0}{h_{2i-1}h_{2i}} + \frac{2u_{2i-1}}{h_{2i-1}(h_{2i-1} + h_{2i})} + \frac{2u_{2i}}{h_{2i}(h_{2i-1} + h_{2i})} \right] = 0.$$

6.3. THE MIXED PROBLEM

Of course, when considering the Mixed Problem in three dimensions, the major considerations to be added to those of Section 6.2 relate to approximating normal derivatives at various points of S_h. For this purpose the positive normal direction at a point of S is defined to be the **outward** direction, if and when such a direction exists.

One could first extend the linear approximation method of Section 3.2. For example, consider the arrangement in Figure 6.2. Assume that the

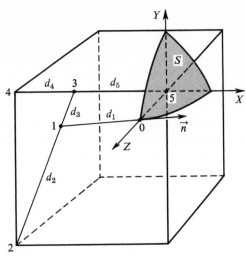

Figure 6.2

normal derivative $\dfrac{\partial u}{\partial n}$ is prescribed at the point of S_h which has been numbered 0 and that

(a) the points 2, 4, and 5 are points of G_h,
(b) 4 and 5 are adjacent and 2 and 4 are adjacent,
(c) 5 is the nearest point (distinct from 0) of G_h to 0 in the z direction,
(d) the segment joining 0 to 5 is in G,
(e) the straight line along the unit normal $\vec{n}$ at 0 meets the plane through 2, 4, and 5 in the point numbered 1,
(f) the straight line through 1 and 2 meets the straight line through 4 and 5 in a point numbered 3,
(g) the distances between 0 and 1; 1 and 2; 1 and 3; 3 and 4; and 3 and 5 are d_1, d_2, d_3, d_4, and d_5, respectively.

Then, by linear interpolation,

$$\frac{\partial u}{\partial n}\bigg|_0 \sim \frac{u_0 - u_1}{d} = \frac{u_0}{d} - \frac{1}{d}(u_1) \sim \frac{u_0}{d} - \frac{1}{d}\left[\frac{d_3 u_2 + d_2 u_3}{d_2 + d_3}\right]$$

$$= \frac{u_0}{d} - \frac{d_3}{d(d_2 + d_3)} u_2 - \frac{d_2}{d(d_2 + d_3)} u_3$$

$$\sim \frac{u_0}{d} - \frac{d_3}{d(d_2 + d_3)} u_2 - \frac{d_2}{d(d_2 + d_3)}\left[\frac{d_4 u_5 + d_5 u_4}{d_4 + d_5}\right],$$

so that an approximation is

$$(6.4) \quad \left.\frac{\partial u}{\partial n}\right|_0 = \frac{u_0}{d} - \frac{d_3}{d(d_2 + d_3)} u_2 - \frac{d_2 d_4}{d(d_2 + d_3)(d_4 + d_5)} u_5$$

$$- \frac{d_2 d_5}{d(d_2 + d_3)(d_4 + d_5)} u_4.$$

Similar formulas follow easily for other arrangements of points.

Application of approximations like (6.4) yields, as in Chapter 3, a unique numerical solution and convergence to a suitably differentiable

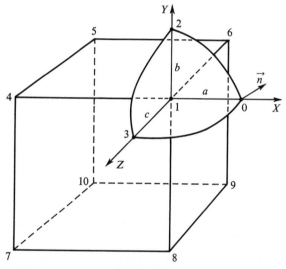

Figure 6.3

analytical solution. However, in practice, actual numerical results have been far too inaccurate by almost any standard. Where applicable, a generalization of the second order formulas (3.6) and (3.10) has proved far more successful, so such formulas will be derived next.

As shown in Figure 6.3, let the point $(x,y,z) \in S_h$ be numbered 0 and assume an arrangement of points of G_h like that shown. Let the indicated cube with vertices 1, 4, 5, 6, 7, 8, 9, 10 have edge equal to h and let $0 < a \leq h$, $0 < b \leq h$, $0 < c \leq h$. The coordinates of the points 0, 1, $\cdots$, 10 are then, respectively, (x,y,z), $(x - a, y, z)$, $(x - a, y + b, z)$ $(x - a, y, z + c)$, $(x - a - h, y, z)$, $(x - a - h, y, z - h)$, $(x - a, y, z - c)$, $(x - a - h, y - h, z)$, $(x - a, y - h, z)$, $(x - a, y - h, z - h)$, and $(x - a - h, y - h, z - h)$.

Now at (x,y,z) set

(6.5)
$$\frac{\partial u}{\partial n} \equiv \sum_0^9 \alpha_i u_i.$$

Since

(6.6)
$$\frac{\partial u}{\partial n} = u_x \cos \alpha + u_y \cos \beta + u_z \cos \gamma,$$

where $\cos \alpha$, $\cos \beta$, and $\cos \gamma$ are direction cosines of $\vec{n}$, it follows by substitution of finite Taylor expansions about (x,y,z) into (6.5) that

(6.7) $u_x \cos \alpha + u_y \cos \beta + u_z \cos \gamma$

$$\equiv u_0(\alpha_0 + \alpha_1 + \alpha_2 + \alpha_3 + \alpha_4 + \alpha_5 + \alpha_6 + \alpha_7 + \alpha_8 + \alpha_9)$$
$$+ u_x[-a\alpha_1 - a\alpha_2 - a\alpha_3 - (a+h)\alpha_4 - (a+h)\alpha_5 - a\alpha_6$$
$$- (a+h)\alpha_7 - a\alpha_8 - a\alpha_9]$$
$$+ u_y[b\alpha_2 - h\alpha_7 - h\alpha_8 - h\alpha_9]$$
$$+ u_z[c\alpha_3 - h\alpha_5 - h\alpha_6 - h\alpha_9]$$
$$+ \tfrac{1}{2}u_{xx}[a^2\alpha_1 + a^2\alpha_2 + a^2\alpha_3 + (a+h)^2\alpha_4 + (a+h)^2\alpha_5$$
$$+ a^2\alpha_6 + (a+h)^2\alpha_7 + a^2\alpha_8 + a^2\alpha_9]$$
$$+ \tfrac{1}{2}u_{yy}[b^2\alpha_2 + h^2\alpha_7 + h^2\alpha_8 + h^2\alpha_9]$$
$$+ \tfrac{1}{2}u_{zz}[c^2\alpha_3 + h^2\alpha_5 + h^2\alpha_6 + h^2\alpha_9]$$
$$+ u_{xy}[-ab\alpha_2 + h(a+h)\alpha_7 + ah\alpha_8 + ah\alpha_9]$$
$$+ u_{xz}[-ac\alpha_3 + h(a+h)\alpha_5 + ah\alpha_6 + ah\alpha_9]$$
$$+ u_{yz}[h^2\alpha_9] + O(\alpha_i h^3).$$

Setting corresponding coefficients in (6.7) equal yields the ten linear algebraic equations in the ten unknowns $\alpha_0, \cdots, \alpha_9$:

(6.8) $\alpha_0 + \alpha_1 + \alpha_2 + \alpha_3 + \alpha_4 + \alpha_5 + \alpha_6 + \alpha_7 + \alpha_8 + \alpha_9 = 0,$

$$-a\alpha_1 - a\alpha_2 - a\alpha_3 - (a+h)\alpha_4 - (a+h)\alpha_5 - a\alpha_6$$
$$- (a+h)\alpha_7 - a\alpha_8 - a\alpha_9 = \cos \alpha,$$
$$b\alpha_2 - h\alpha_7 - h\alpha_8 - h\alpha_9 = \cos \beta,$$
$$c\alpha_3 - h\alpha_5 - h\alpha_6 - h\alpha_9 = \cos \gamma,$$

$$a^2\alpha_1 + a^2\alpha_2 + a^2\alpha_3 + (a + h)^2\alpha_4 + (a + h)^2\alpha_5 + a^2\alpha_6$$
$$+ (a + h)^2\alpha_7 + a^2\alpha_8 + a^2\alpha_9 = 0,$$
$$b^2\alpha_2 + h^2\alpha_7 + h^2\alpha_8 + h^2\alpha_9 = 0,$$
$$c^2\alpha_3 + h^2\alpha_5 + h^2\alpha_6 + h^2\alpha_9 = 0,$$
$$-ab\alpha_2 + h(a + h)\alpha_7 + ah\alpha_8 + ah\alpha_9 = 0,$$
$$-ac\alpha_3 + h(a + h)\alpha_5 + ah\alpha_6 + ah\alpha_9 = 0,$$
$$h^2\alpha_9 = 0.$$

The solution of system (6.8) is

$$\alpha_0 = \frac{(2a + h)}{a(a + h)} \cos \alpha,$$

$$\alpha_1 = -\frac{(a + h)}{ah} \cos \alpha + \frac{(hb - h^2 + ab)}{bh^2} \cos \beta + \frac{(hc - h^2 + ac)}{h^2 c} \cos \gamma,$$

$$\alpha_2 = \frac{h}{b(b + h)} \cos \beta, \qquad \alpha_3 = \frac{h}{c(c + h)} \cos \gamma,$$

(6.9)

$$\alpha_4 = \frac{a}{h(a + h)} \cos \alpha - \frac{a}{h^2} \cos \gamma - \frac{a}{h^2} \cos \beta, \qquad \alpha_5 = \frac{a}{h^2} \cos \gamma,$$

$$\alpha_6 = -\frac{hc + ac + ah}{h^2(c + h)} \cos \gamma, \qquad \alpha_7 = \frac{a}{h^2} \cos \beta,$$

$$\alpha_8 = -\frac{hb + ab + ah}{h^2(b + h),} \cos \beta, \qquad \alpha_9 = 0.$$

Thus, the desired approximation is given by (6.5) where the α_i are given by (6.9).

If the normal derivative is prescribed at the point numbered 3 in Figure 6.3, then the approximation for $\frac{\partial u}{\partial n}$ can be obtained easily from (6.5) and (6.9) by considering the transformation $z \to x, x \to y, y \to z$. If the normal derivative is prescribed at the point numbered 2 in Figure 6.3, then the approximation follows easily by considering the transformation $y \to x$, $x \to z, z \to y$.

Note that if in (6.5) the summation had been taken from 0 to 10, then (6.8) would have been a system of 10 equations in the eleven unknowns $\alpha_0, \alpha_1, \cdots, \alpha_{10}$. By setting $\alpha_{10} = 0$, one would have deduced (6.9). By not

TABLE 6.1

x	y	z	Approximate Solution $U^{(1)}$	Approximate Solution $U^{(2)}$	Exact Solution $u = x^3y - xy^3 + 5z$
.1	.1	.1	−0.50000000	−0.50000000	−0.50000000
.1	.1	.7	−3.50000000	−3.50000000	−3.50000000
.1	.2	.2	−1.00059993	−1.00060000	−1.00060000
.1	.3	.1	−0.50239984	−0.50239998	−0.50240000
.1	.3	.6	−3.00239930	−3.00239992	−3.00240000
.1	.4	.2	−1.00599922	−1.00599990	−1.00600000
.1	.4	.8	−4.00599842	−4.00599974	−4.00600000
.1	.6	.2	−1.02099693	−1.02099962	−1.02100000
.1	.7	.1	−0.53359660	−0.53359961	−0.53360000
.1	.7	.7	−3.53361012	−3.53360023	−3.53360000
.1	.8	.4	−2.05039221	−2.05039855	−2.05040000
.2	.1	.1	−0.49940004	−0.49940000	−0.49940000
.2	.1	.6	−2.99940018	−2.99940002	−2.99940000
.2	.2	.1	−0.50000000	−0.50000000	−0.50000000
.2	.2	.6	−3.00000000	−3.00000000	−3.00000000
.2	.3	.1	−0.50299980	−0.50299997	−0.50300000
.2	.4	.1	−0.50959933	−0.50959992	−0.50960000
.2	.4	.6	−3.00959709	−3.00959968	−3.00960000
.2	.5	.5	−2.52099448	−2.52099937	−2.52100000
.2	.6	.2	−1.03839447	−1.03839930	−1.03840000
.2	.6	.6	−3.03838782	−3.03839868	−3.03840000
.2	.7	.6	−3.06297700	−3.06299759	−3.06300000
.3	.1	.1	−0.49760016	−0.49760002	−0.49760000
.3	.1	.6	−2.99760070	−2.99760008	−2.99760000
.3	.2	.1	−0.49700020	−0.49700002	−0.49700000
.3	.2	.6	−2.99700092	−2.99700010	−2.99700000
.3	.3	.1	−0.50000000	−0.50000000	−0.50000000
.3	.3	.9	−4.50000000	−4.50000000	−4.50000000
.3	.4	.8	−4.00839981	−4.00839951	−4.00840000
.3	.5	.6	−3.02399285	−3.02399923	−3.02400000
.3	.6	.4	−2.04858917	−2.04859867	−2.04860000
.3	.7	.3	−1.58398473	−1.58399789	−1.58400000
.3	.8	.2	−1.13198012	−1.13199693	−1.13200000
.3	.9	.2	−1.19437299	−1.19439290	−1.19440000
.4	.1	.4	−1.99400130	−1.99400016	−1.99400000

TABLE 6.1 (*Continued*)

x	y	z	Approximate Solution $U^{(1)}$	Approximate Solution $U^{(2)}$	Exact Solution $u = x^3y - xy^3 + 5z$
.4	.1	.8	−3.99400158	−3.99400026	−3.99400000
.4	.2	.8	−3.99040373	−3.99040039	−3.99040000
.4	.3	.5	−2.49160217	−2.49160024	−2.49160000
.4	.4	.1	−0.50000000	−0.50000000	−0.50000000
.4	.5	.2	−1.01799753	−1.01799967	−1.01800000
.4	.6	.4	−2.04798864	−2.04799869	−2.04800000
.4	.7	.3	−1.59238087	−1.59239767	−1.59240000
.4	.8	.4	−2.15360595	−2.15359356	−2.15360000
.5	.1	.7	−3.48800346	−3.48800042	−3.48800000
.5	.2	.5	−2.47900552	−2.47900062	−2.47900000
.5	.3	.3	−1.47600437	−1.47600055	−1.47600000
.5	.4	.3	−1.48200338	−1.48200042	−1.48200000
.5	.5	.1	−0.50000000	−0.50000000	−0.50000000
.5	.5	.7	−3.50000000	−3.50000000	−3.50000000
.5	.7	.2	−1.08398798	−1.08399811	−1.08400000
.6	.1	.2	−0.97900307	−0.97900037	−0.97900000
.6	.1	.6	−2.97900485	−2.97900064	−2.97900000
.6	.2	.4	−1.96160854	−1.96160104	−1.96160000
.6	.3	.2	−0.95140680	−0.95140090	−0.95140000
.6	.3	.6	−2.95141421	−2.95140156	−2.95140000
.6	.4	.5	−2.45201490	−2.45200137	−2.45200000
.6	.5	.5	−2.46700303	−2.46700050	−2.46700000
.6	.6	.4	−2.00000000	−2.00000000	−2.00000000
.7	.1	.4	−1.96640694	−1.96640094	−1.96640000
.7	.2	.3	−1.43701210	−1.43700156	−1.43700000
.7	.3	.2	−0.91601231	−0.91600171	−0.91600000
.7	.4	.1	−0.40760854	−0.40760124	−0.40760000
.7	.4	.5	−2.40764318	−2.40760312	−2.40760000
.7	.5	.5	−2.41599728	−2.41599952	−2.41600000
.7	.7	.1	−0.50000000	−0.50000000	−0.50000000
.8	.2	.1	−0.40401347	−0.40400140	−0.40400000
.8	.3	.4	−1.86803535	−1.86800377	−1.86800000
.8	.5	.1	−0.34404041	−0.34400209	−0.34400000
.9	.1	.4	−1.92799112	−1.92800167	−1.92800000
.9	.4	.1	−0.26598085	−0.26599834	−0.26600000

setting $\alpha_{10} = 0$, other second order approximations can be found. Note, however, from (6.9), that not only is the point numbered 10 unnecessary for such an approximation, but so is the point numbered 9.

6.4. EXAMPLES

Typical numerical support will now be presented by means of several examples, each of which was run on the CDC 1604.

Example 1. In E^3, let G be the spherical sector in the first octant bounded by the surfaces whose equations are $x = 0, y = 0, z = 0, x^2 + y^2 + z^2 = 1$. Consider the Dirichlet Problem of Section 6.2 with $\phi = x^2 + 2y - z^2$. Set $(\bar{x}, \bar{y}, \bar{z}) = (0,0,0)$ and $h = .1$. R_h contains 410 points. Using over-relaxation with $\omega = 1.8$ and zero initial vector, the numerical method of Section 6.2 yielded results correct to *at least* nine decimal places to the exact solution $u = x^2 + 2y - z^2$. The running time was 1 minute, 50 seconds.

Example 2. Example 1 was modified by setting $\phi = x^3y - xy^3 - 5z$. Selected, but typical, results are recorded under $U^{(1)}$ in Table 6.1. The running time was 1 minute, 53 seconds and the exact solution was $u = x^3y - xy^3 - 5z$.

Example 3. Example 2 was modified by refining the grid to $h = .05$. Selected, but typical, results are recorded under $U^{(2)}$ in Table 6.1. The running time was 8 minutes, 11 seconds.

Example 4. In E^4, let G be the spherical sector defined as the set of all (x,y,z,w) whose coordinates satisfy $x \geq 0$, $y \geq 0$, $z \geq 0$, $w \geq 0$, $x^2 + y^2 + z^2 + w^2 \leq 1$. Consider the Dirichlet Problem for (6.1') with $n = 4$ and with $\phi = x^2 - 2y^2 + 3z^2 - 2w^2$. Set $(\bar{x}, \bar{y}, \bar{z}, \bar{w}) = (0,0,0,0)$, $h = .1$. R_h contains 803 points. The difference approximation (6.3) of the four dimensional Laplace equation is

$$\sum_{i=1}^{4} \left[\frac{-2u_0}{h_{2i-1}h_{2i}} + \frac{2u_{2i-1}}{h_{2i-1}(h_{2i-1} + h_{2i})} + \frac{2u_{2i}}{h_{2i}(h_{2i-1} + h_{2i})} \right] = 0.$$

Using over-relaxation with $\omega = 1.8$ and zero initial vector, the numerical method of Section 6.2 approximated the exact solution $u = x^2 - 2y^2 + 3z^2 - 2w^2$ at each point to at least nine decimal places. The running time was 3 minutes, 58 seconds.

Example 5. In this example we will show how the method of Section 6.2 can be applied in E^3 even when R is not homeomorphic to the interior of the unit sphere. Let S_1 be the outer cubic surface with vertices $(0,0,0)$, $(2,0,0)$, $(0,2,0)$, $(0,0,2)$, $(2,2,0)$, $(2,0,2)$, $(0,2,2)$, and $(2,2,2)$ and let S_2 be the inner cubic surface with vertices $(\frac{1}{2},\frac{1}{2},\frac{1}{2})$, $(\frac{3}{2},\frac{1}{2},\frac{1}{2})$, $(\frac{1}{2},\frac{3}{2},\frac{1}{2})$, $(\frac{1}{2},\frac{1}{2},\frac{3}{2})$, $(\frac{3}{2},\frac{3}{2},\frac{1}{2})$, $(\frac{3}{2},\frac{1}{2},\frac{3}{2})$, $(\frac{1}{2},\frac{3}{2},\frac{1}{2})$, and $(\frac{3}{2},\frac{3}{2},\frac{3}{2})$, as shown in Figure 6.4. Let R be the region between S_1 and S_2. Let $S = S_1 \cup S_2$ and $G = R \cup S$. Also, it is given that $\phi \equiv 1$ on S_1, $\phi \equiv 0$ on S_2. Then, setting $(\bar{x},\bar{y},\bar{z}) = (0,0,0)$ and $h = .1$, the method of Section 6.2 was applied to the resulting

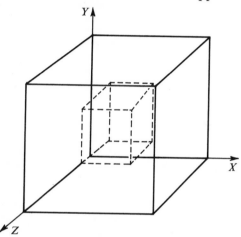

Figure 6.4

Dirichlet Problem. R_h contained 784 points. The symmetry of the solution was incorporated into the program so that only one-eighth of G had to be considered. Over-relaxation was applied with $\omega = 1.8$ and zero initial vector, and selected, but typical, results are recorded under $U^{(1)}$ of Table 6.2. The running time was 2 minutes, 26 seconds. (Note that, of course, the rigorous mathematical basis outlined in Section 6.2 does not apply in entirety to this example.)

Example 6. Example 5 was modified by refining the grid to $h = .05$. R_h contained 6669 points. Selected, but typical, results are recorded under $U^{(2)}$ in Table 6.2. The running time was 12 minutes, 49 seconds.

Example 7. In E^3, let G be the spherical sector in the first octant bounded by the surfaces with equations $x = 0$, $y = 0$, $z = 0$ and

TABLE 6.2

x	y	z	$U^{(1)}$	$U^{(2)}$
1.0	1.0	1.6	.21318413	.21340617
1.0	1.4	1.6	.25474801	.26000151
1.0	1.6	1.3	.23039266	.23203625
1.0	1.8	1.9	.93922824	.94029832
1.0	1.9	1.6	.87962760	.88193903
1.1	1.5	1.7	.52860578	.53955766
1.1	1.6	1.6	.46730212	.47796716
1.1	1.8	1.5	.70210223	.70815556
1.1	1.9	1.0	.81346190	.81395052
1.2	1.1	1.9	.81812623	.81902279
1.2	1.6	1.1	.22076057	.22147398
1.2	1.7	1.1	.43191770	.43329169
1.2	1.8	1.1	.63036172	.63180745
1.2	1.9	1.7	.91165183	.91351895
1.3	1.5	1.7	.54872314	.56194398
1.3	1.7	1.5	.54872314	.56194398
1.3	1.8	1.2	.64900339	.65215013
1.4	1.0	1.7	.47342317	.47933409
1.4	1.2	1.8	.67122668	.67620583
1.4	1.6	1.4	.29590727	.30704619
1.4	1.8	1.9	.94863874	.95008233
1.5	1.2	1.6	.31897168	.33873950
1.5	1.6	1.5	.41057277	.45137840
1.5	1.8	1.4	.73764103	.74655664
1.5	1.9	1.6	.90921585	.91255196
1.6	1.1	1.8	.75512719	.76003480
1.6	1.2	1.9	.88318714	.88577147
1.6	1.5	1.6	.56670759	.58864922
1.6	1.7	1.6	.75991236	.76967969
1.6	1.9	1.3	.88834726	.89126535
1.7	1.0	1.0	.42086795	.42134851
1.7	1.2	1.0	.42989416	.43111151
1.7	1.4	1.3	.49616024	.50444129
1.7	1.6	1.5	.70081037	.71379555
1.7	1.8	1.5	.86041861	.86533931
1.8	1.1	1.3	.64295832	.64555233
1.8	1.2	1.7	.82021476	.82397741
1.8	1.4	1.4	.70371313	.71143949
1.8	1.6	1.7	.88560303	.88971671
1.8	1.9	1.3	.94416441	.94549284
1.9	1.0	1.4	.83606017	.83822357
1.9	1.3	1.1	.82513613	.82661512
1.9	1.3	1.7	.91578506	.91787661
1.9	1.5	1.7	.93179483	.93410454
1.9	1.7	1.0	.90873890	.91041024
1.9	1.9	1.0	.96974268	.97026699

TABLE 6.3

x	y	z	Approximate Solution	Exact Solution $u = x^2 - 3y^2 + 2z^2$
.15000	.15000	.15000	.000000	.000000
.15000	.15000	.75000	1.080000	1.080000
.15000	.30000	.45000	.157499	.157500
.15000	.30000	.94207	1.527500	1.527500
.15000	.45000	.75000	.540000	.540000
.15000	.60000	.60000	−.337499	−.337500
.15000	.75000	.15000	−1.620000	−1.620000
.27839	.75000	.60000	−.889999	−.890000
.15000	.90000	.30000	−2.227500	−2.227500
.30000	.15000	.45000	.427500	.427500
.30000	.15000	.94207	1.797500	1.797500
.30000	.30000	.75000	.945000	.945000
.30000	.45000	.15000	−.472499	−.472500
.30000	.58949	.75000	.172500	.172500
.30000	.60000	.60000	−.269999	−.270000
.30000	.75000	.45000	−1.192500	−1.192500
.30000	.94207	.15000	−2.527500	−2.527500
.45000	.15000	.15000	.180000	.180000
.45000	.15000	.88034	1.684999	1.685000
.45000	.45000	.45000	.000000	.000000
.45000	.45000	.77136	.785000	.785000
.52915	.60000	.60000	−.079999	−.080000
.45000	.77136	.45000	−1.177499	−1.177500
.60000	.15000	.60000	1.012500	1.012500
.60000	.30000	.15000	.135000	.135000
.60000	.30000	.74162	1.190000	1.190000
.66144	.45000	.60000	.550000	.550000
.74162	.60000	.30000	−.349999	−.350000
.60000	.60000	.52915	−.159999	−.160000
.75000	.15000	.15000	.540000	.540000
.75000	.45000	.30000	.135000	.135000
.75000	.48477	.45000	.262500	.262500
.75000	.60000	.27839	−.362499	−.362500
.90554	.30000	.30000	.730000	.730000

$x^2 + y^2 + z^2 = 1$. The boundary conditions are $\phi = x^2 - 3y^2$ on the xy-face, $\phi = x^2 + 2z^2$ on the xz-face, $\phi = -3y^2 + 2z^2$ on the yz-face, $\dfrac{\partial u}{\partial n} = 2x^2 - 6y^2 + 4z^2$ on the spherical portion. Let $(\bar{x},\bar{y},\bar{z}) = (0,0,0)$ and $h = .15$. At each point of R_h, (6.2) was applied while at each point of S_h whose coordinates satisfied $x^2 + y^2 + z^2 = 1$, $x \neq 0$, $y \neq 0$, $z \neq 0$, (6.5) and (6.9), or the appropriate modification, was applied. The resulting system of 192 equations was solved by Gaussian elimination. The running time was 7 minutes, 11 seconds and typical results are recorded in Table 6.3. Accuracy was unusually good because all derivatives of order three or more of the exact solution are zero.

Example 8. Example 7 was modified by applying successive over-relaxation with $\omega = .1, .2, \cdots, 1.7, 1.8$, and 1.9 and initial vectors zero and one. In all 38 cases the iteration diverged.

EXERCISES

1. Show that if (a,b,c) is a fixed point in E^3, then at each point of E^3 except (a,b,c)
$$u = [(x - a)^2 + (y - b)^2 + (z - c)^2]^{-1/2}$$
is a solution of $u_{xx} + u_{yy} + u_{zz} = 0$.

2. Show that in spherical polar coordinates r,θ,ϕ, the Laplace equation $u_{xx} + u_{yy} + u_{zz} = 0$ takes the form
$$\frac{\partial^2 u}{\partial r^2} + \frac{2}{r}\frac{\partial u}{\partial r} + \frac{1}{r^2}\frac{\partial^2 u}{\partial \theta^2} + \frac{\cot \theta}{r^2}\frac{\partial u}{\partial \theta} + \frac{1}{r^2 \sin^2 \theta}\frac{\partial^2 u}{\partial \phi^2} = 0.$$

3. (a) Show that if U_i is defined on $R_h \cup S_h$ and satisfies (6.2) at each point of R_h, then U_i possesses a strong max–min property on $R_h \cup S_h$.
(b) Repeat part (a) but for (6.3) instead of (6.2).

4. In E^3 let G be the spherical sector in the first octant bounded by the surfaces whose equations are $x = 0$, $y = 0$, $z = 0$, $x^2 + y^2 + z^2 = 1$. Consider the Dirichlet Problem of Section 6.2 with $\phi = x^2 + 2y - z^2$. Find an approximate solution on R_h for each of the following.

(a) $(\bar{x},\bar{y},\bar{z}) = (0,0,0)$ and $h = .3$.
(b) $(\bar{x},\bar{y},\bar{z}) = (0,0,0)$ and $h = .2$.

Compare each approximate solution with the exact solution $u = x^2 + 2y - z^2$.

5. Let G be defined as in Exercise 4. Consider the Dirichlet Problem of Section 6.2 with $\phi = x^3y - xy^3 - 5z$. Find an approximate solution on R_h for each of the following.

(a) $(\bar{x},\bar{y},\bar{z}) = (0,0,0)$ and $h = .3$.
(b) $(\bar{x},\bar{y},\bar{z}) = (0,0,0)$ and $h = .2$.

Compare each approximate solution with the exact solution

$$u = x^3y - xy^3 - 5z.$$

6. Let G be defined as in Exercise 4. Let $\phi = x^2 - 3y^2$ on the xy-face, $\phi = x^2 + 2z^2$ on the xz-face, $\phi = -3y^2 + 2z^2$ on the yz-face, $\dfrac{\partial u}{\partial n} = 2x^2 - 6y^2 + 4z^2$ on the spherical portion. Let $(\bar{x},\bar{y},\bar{z}) = (0,0,0)$ and $h = .3$. At each point of R_h apply (6.2), while at each point of S_h whose coordinates satisfy $x^2 + y^2 + z^2 = 1$, $x \neq 0$, $y \neq 0$, $z \neq 0$ apply (6.5) and (6.9) or the appropriate modification. Solve the resulting system of algebraic equations. Compare the resulting approximate solution of the given Mixed Problem with the exact solution $u = x^2 - 3y^2 + 2z^2$.

7. Derive (3.9) from (6.9).

CHAPTER 7

NONLINEAR PROBLEMS

7.1. INTRODUCTION

As instruments of measurement, like the electron microscope and ammonia clock, become more and more precise, the need to deal with the nonlinear model has become increasingly the rule rather than the exception. However, unlike linear problems, nonlinear problems do not seem amenable at present to a unified or comprehensive treatment. The emphasis in this chapter will be on the numerical treatment of certain mildly nonlinear, three dimensional Dirichlet problems which have physical interest. Extensive use in the proofs will be made of ideas developed by Bers [1]. Other nonlinear elliptic equations will be discussed in Sections 7.9 and 7.10.

7.2. ANALYTICAL PRELIMINARIES

Let R be a bounded region that is homeomorphic to the interior of the unit sphere. Denote the boundary of R by S and let $G = R \cup S$.

Definition 7.1
Let $F(x,y,z,t,p,q,r) \in C^1$ for all $(x,y,z) \in R$ and for all real t, p, q, r. If for all t

(7.1) $$F_t \geq 0$$

and for all p, q and r there exists a constant A such that

(7.2) $|F_p|, |F_q|, |F_r| \leq A,$

then the elliptic equation

(7.3) $u_{xx} + u_{yy} + u_{zz} = F(x,y,z,u,u_x,u_y,u_z)$

is said to be mildly nonlinear on R.

Example
$u_{xx} + u_{yy} + u_{zz} = e^u$ is mildly nonlinear on every possible R.

Definition 7.2
Let $\phi(x,y,z) \in C(S)$. Then a mildly nonlinear Dirichlet problem is that of finding $u(x,y,z)$ which satisfies the three conditions

(a) u is a solution of (7.3) on R,

(b) $u \equiv \phi$ on S,

(c) $u \in [C^2(R) \cap C(G)]$.

Under sufficiently strong smoothness hypotheses (which are more severe than those required for linear equations), a mildly nonlinear Dirichlet problem has a unique solution (see, e.g., Courant and Hilbert [1], Miranda [3]) and it is with such problems that we will be concerned first.

7.3. A NUMERICAL METHOD

Suppose at (x,y,z) in Figure 6.1 one wishes to derive an approximation for u_x. For this purpose set

$$\sum_0^2 \alpha_i u_i = u_x.$$

Substitution of finite Taylor expansions about (x,y,z) for u_1 and u_2 and reorganization of terms then implies, as in Section 2.2,

$$\alpha_0 + \alpha_1 + \alpha_2 = 0$$
$$h_1\alpha_1 - h_2\alpha_2 = 1$$
$$h_1^2\alpha_1 + h_2^2\alpha_2 = 0.$$

The solution of this linear system is

$$\alpha_0 = \frac{h_1 - h_2}{h_1 h_2}, \quad \alpha_1 = \frac{h_2}{h_1(h_1 + h_2)}, \quad \alpha_2 = -\frac{h_1}{h_2(h_1 + h_2)},$$

thus yielding the approximation

$$(7.4) \quad u_x \sim u_{x,h} = \frac{h_1 - h_2}{h_1 h_2} u_0 + \frac{h_2}{h_1(h_1 + h_2)} u_1 - \frac{h_1}{h_2(h_1 + h_2)} u_2.$$

Similarly,

$$(7.5) \quad u_y \sim u_{y,h} = \frac{h_3 - h_4}{h_3 h_4} u_0 + \frac{h_4}{h_3(h_3 + h_4)} u_3 - \frac{h_3}{h_4(h_3 + h_4)} u_4$$

and

$$(7.6) \quad u_z \sim u_{z,h} = \frac{h_5 - h_6}{h_5 h_6} u_0 + \frac{h_6}{h_5(h_5 + h_6)} u_5 - \frac{h_5}{h_6(h_5 + h_6)} u_6.$$

If then, motivated by (2.6), (6.2), and (6.3), one sets

(7.7)

$$u_{xx} + u_{yy} + u_{zz} \sim \Delta_h u = \left(-\frac{2}{h_1 h_2} - \frac{2}{h_3 h_4} - \frac{2}{h_5 h_6} \right) u_0 + \frac{2}{h_1(h_1 + h_2)} u_1$$

$$+ \frac{2}{h_2(h_1 + h_2)} u_2 + \frac{2}{h_3(h_3 + h_4)} u_3 + \frac{2}{h_4(h_3 + h_4)} u_4 + \frac{2}{h_5(h_5 + h_6)} u_5$$

$$+ \frac{2}{h_6(h_5 + h_6)} u_6,$$

then an approximation for (7.3) at point (x,y,z) in Figure 6.1 is given by

$$(7.8) \quad \Delta_h u = F(x,y,z,u,u_{x,h},u_{y,h},u_{z,h}),$$

where $\Delta_h u$, $u_{x,h}$, $u_{y,h}$, $u_{z,h}$ are given in (7.4)–(7.7).

The numerical method is now formulated as follows:

Step 1. Construct R_h, S_h, and G_h as described in Section 6.2 and number the points as there indicated.

Step 2. At each point $(x,y,z) \in S_h$, set $U(x,y,z) = \phi(x,y,z)$.

Step 3. At each point $(x,y,z) \in R_h$, write down in correct subscript notation

$$(7.9) \quad \Delta_h U = F(x,y,z,U,U_{x,h},U_{y,h},U_{z,h}),$$

incorporating the known results of Step 2 wherever possible.

Step 4. Step 3 yields m nonlinear algebraic or transcendental equations in the m unknowns U_1, U_2, $\cdots$, U_m. Solve this system.

Step 5. Let the results of Steps 2 and 4 constitute the approximate solution on G_h.

7.4. AN INEQUALITY FOR A LINEAR DIFFERENCE EQUATION

The questions of existence of the numerical solution and of convergence to the analytical solution will be treated by applying certain relationships which are extensions of results of Chapter 2 and which will be developed next.

Definition 7.3

Let $\alpha^{(i)} = \alpha^{(i)}(x,y,z,t,p,q,r)$, $i = 1$, 2, 3, and $\gamma = \gamma(x,y,z,t,p,q,r)$ be continuous, bounded functions for all $(x,y,z) \in R$ and all real t, p, q, and r. For all $(x,y,z) \in R$ and all t, p, q, and r, let

$$(7.10) \qquad\qquad |\alpha^{(i)}| \leq A, \qquad i = 1, 2, 3,$$

and

$$(7.11) \qquad\qquad \gamma \geq 0,$$

where A is given by (7.2). Then if v is defined on G_h, we define linear operators l_h and $\tilde{l}_h$ at each point $(x,y,z) \in R_h$, as shown in Figure 6.1, by

$$(7.12) \quad l_h[v(x,y,z)]$$
$$= \Delta_h v(x,y,z) + \alpha^{(1)}(x,y,z,t,p,q,r)v_{x,h}(x,y,z)$$
$$+ \alpha^{(2)}(x,y,z,t,p,q,r)v_{y,h}(x,y,z) + \alpha^{(3)}(x,y,z,t,p,q,r)v_{z,h}(x,y,z)$$
$$- \gamma(x,y,z,t,p,q,r)v(x,y,z),$$

$$(7.13) \qquad \tilde{l}_h[v(x,y,z)] = l_h[v(x,y,z)] + \gamma(x,y,z,t,p,q,r)v(x,y,z).$$

Lemma 7.1 (Weak Max–Min Property)

Let $v(x,y,z)$ be defined on G_h and satisfy, independently of t, p, q, and r,

$$(7.14) \qquad\qquad l_h[v] = 0$$

at each point of R_h. Then, if h satisfies

$$(7.15) \qquad\qquad Ah < 2\theta, \qquad 0 < \theta < \tfrac{1}{4}$$

for some constant θ, it follows that for $(x,y,z) \in G_h$

(7.16)
$$\min (0, \min_{S_h} v) \le v(x, y, z) \le \max (0, \max_{S_h} v)$$

and, in particular,

(7.17)
$$\max_{R_h} |v| \le \max_{S_h} |v| .$$

Proof:

For $(x,y,z) \in R_h$, (7.14) can be written in the equivalent form

(7.18)
$$
v_0 \left[-\frac{2}{h_1 h_2} - \frac{2}{h_3 h_4} - \frac{2}{h_5 h_6} + \alpha^{(1)} \frac{h_1 - h_2}{h_1 h_2} + \alpha^{(2)} \frac{h_3 - h_4}{h_3 h_4} \right.
$$
$$
\left. + \alpha^{(3)} \frac{h_5 - h_6}{h_5 h_6} - \gamma \right]
$$
$$
+ v_1 \left[\frac{2 + \alpha^{(1)} h_2}{h_1 (h_1 + h_2)} \right] + v_2 \left[\frac{2 - \alpha^{(1)} h_1}{h_2 (h_1 + h_2)} \right] + v_3 \left[\frac{2 + \alpha^{(2)} h_4}{h_3 (h_3 + h_4)} \right]
$$
$$
+ v_4 \left[\frac{2 - \alpha^{(2)} h_3}{h_4 (h_3 + h_4)} \right] + v_5 \left[\frac{2 + \alpha^{(3)} h_6}{h_5 (h_5 + h_6)} \right] + v_6 \left[\frac{2 - \alpha^{(3)} h_5}{h_6 (h_5 + h_6)} \right] = 0.
$$

By (7.15) it follows that Lemma 2.1 applies to (7.18) and the result follows in the same fashion as in Lemma 2.3.

The ideas of Chapter 2 will now be extended under the assumption that $Ah < 2\theta$.

Lemma 7.2

If h satisfies (7.15), the linear algebraic system

(7.19)
$$l_h[U_i] = k_i, \qquad i = 1, 2, \cdots, m$$
$$U_j = \phi_j, \qquad j = m + 1, \cdots, m + n$$

has a unique solution given by

(7.20)
$$U_i = \sum_{s=1}^{m} G^{is} k_s + \sum_{j=1}^{n} \Gamma^{ij} U_{j+m}, \qquad i = 1, 2, \cdots, m,$$

where G^{is} and Γ^{is} depend only on t, p, q, r, and G_h. Every function v defined on G_h satisfies

(7.21)
$$v_i = \sum_{s=1}^{m} G^{is} l_h[v_s] + \sum_{j=1}^{n} \Gamma^{ij} v_{j+m}, \qquad i = 1, 2, \cdots, m,$$

so that for each fixed t, p, q, and r

$$(7.22) \qquad \max_{R_h} |v| \leq \left\{ \max_{R_h} |l_h[v]| \right\} \left\{ \max_i \sum_{s=1}^m |G^{is}| \right\}$$

$$+ \left\{ \max_{S_h} |v| \right\} \left\{ \max_i \sum_{j=1}^n |\Gamma^{ij}| \right\}, \qquad i = 1, 2, \cdots, m.$$

Moreover, independently of t, p, q, and r,

$$(7.23) \qquad \max_i \sum_{j=1}^n |\Gamma^{ij}| \leq 1, \qquad i = 1, 2, \cdots, m,$$

and

$$(7.24) \qquad G^{ij} \leq 0, \qquad i = 1, 2, \cdots, m; \quad j = 1, 2, \cdots, m.$$

Proof:

Since for each fixed t, p, q, and r the proof follows as in Theorems 2.2 and 2.3, the theorem follows readily.

Lemma 7.3

Let the matrices $\tilde{G}^{ij}$ and $\tilde{\Gamma}^{ij}$ play the same roles for $\tilde{l}_h$ as G^{ij} and Γ^{ij}, respectively, play for l_h. Then, for each t, p, q, and r

$$(7.25) \qquad \max_i \sum_{s=1}^m |G^{is}| \leq \max_i \sum_{s=1}^m |\tilde{G}^{is}|, \qquad i = 1, 2, \cdots, m.$$

Proof:

First arbitrarily fix t, p, q, and r. Then, analogous to (7.24), one has $\tilde{G}^{ij} \leq 0$. Next, for h satisfying (7.15), the linear algebraic system

$$(7.26) \qquad \begin{aligned} \tilde{l}_h[\tilde{U}_i] &= \delta_{il}, & i &= 1, 2, \cdots, m \\ \tilde{U}_j &= 0, & j &= m+1, \cdots, m+n \end{aligned}$$

has a unique solution given by

$$(7.27) \qquad \tilde{U}_i^{(l)} = \sum_{s=1}^m \tilde{G}^{is} \delta_{sl},$$

where

$$(7.28) \qquad \tilde{U}_i^{(l)} = \tilde{G}^{il} \leq 0.$$

Let $U_i^{(l)}$ be the solution of (7.19) with $k_i = \delta_{il}$, $\phi_j = 0$. Then $U_i^{(l)} = G^{il}$ and

$$\begin{aligned} l_h[U_i^{(l)} - \tilde{U}_i^{(l)}] &= l_h[U_i^{(l)}] - \{\tilde{l}_h[\tilde{U}_i^{(l)}] - \gamma_i \tilde{U}_i^{(l)}\} \\ &= \delta_{il} - \delta_{il} + \gamma_i \tilde{U}_i^{(l)} \\ &= \gamma_i \tilde{G}^{il} \leq 0. \end{aligned}$$

Setting $v_i = U_i^{(l)} - \tilde{U}_i^{(l)}$ in (7.21) implies then that

$$U_i^{(l)} - \tilde{U}_i^{(l)} = \sum_{s=1}^{m} G^{is} l_h[U_s^{(l)} - \tilde{U}_s^{(l)}] \geq 0.$$

Thus,

$$U_i^{(l)} - \tilde{U}_i^{(l)} = G^{il} - \tilde{G}^{il} \geq 0,$$

which implies, for all i and all j

$$|\tilde{G}^{ij}| \geq |G^{ij}|.$$

Thus (7.25) follows readily and the lemma is valid.

One additional lemma will still be necessary before the main results can be established.

Lemma 7.4

On $G = R \cup S$ there exists a nonnegative function $\psi(x,y,z)$ and a constant C, which depends only on A and the diameter d of G, such that for all sufficiently small h (to be described in the proof), it follows that

$$(7.29) \qquad\qquad l_h[\psi] > 0$$

independently of t, p, q, and r. Moreover, for each fixed t, p, q, and r

$$(7.30) \qquad\qquad \frac{\max\limits_{G} \psi}{\min\limits_{R_h} l_h[\psi]} \leq C(A, d).$$

Proof:

Without loss of generality, assume that G is contained between, and has no points in common with, the two planes given by $x = 0$ and $x = d$. Set $\psi(x,y,z) = e^{2Ax}$. Then

$$\Delta_h \psi = 2e^{2Ax}\left[-\frac{1}{h_1 h_2} + \frac{e^{2Ah_1}}{h_1(h_1 + h_2)} + \frac{e^{-2Ah_2}}{h_2(h_1 + h_2)} \right]$$

$$\alpha^{(1)}\psi_{x,h} = \alpha^{(1)}e^{2Ax}\left[\frac{h_1 - h_2}{h_1 h_2} + \frac{h_2}{h_1(h_1 + h_2)} e^{2Ah_1} - \frac{h_1}{h_2(h_1 + h_2)} e^{-2Ah_2} \right]$$

$$\alpha^{(2)}\psi_{y,h} = \alpha^{(3)}\psi_{z,h} = 0.$$

Then

$$(7.31) \quad l_h[\psi] = 2e^{2Ax}\left[-\frac{1}{h_1 h_2} + \frac{e^{2Ah_1}}{h_1(h_1 + h_2)} + \frac{e^{-2Ah_2}}{h_2(h_1 + h_2)} \right]$$

$$+ \alpha^{(1)}e^{2Ax}\left[\frac{h_1 - h_2}{h_1 h_2} + \frac{h_2}{h_1(h_1 + h_2)} e^{2Ah_1} - \frac{h_1}{h_2(h_1 + h_2)} e^{-2Ah_2} \right].$$

But

$$\left[\frac{h_1 - h_2}{h_1 h_2} + \frac{h_2}{h_1(h_1 + h_2)} e^{2Ah_1} - \frac{h_1}{h_2(h_1 + h_2)} e^{-2Ah_2}\right]$$

$$= \frac{1}{h_1 h_2(h_1 + h_2)} [h_1^2 - h_2^2 + h_2^2 e^{2Ah_1} - h_1^2 e^{-2Ah_2}]$$

$$= \frac{1}{h_1 h_2(h_1 + h_2)} [h_1^2(1 - e^{-2Ah_2}) + h_2^2(e^{2Ah_1} - 1)] > 0,$$

so that, with regard to (7.31), one has

$$(7.32) \quad l_h[\psi] \geq 2e^{2Ax}\left[-\frac{1}{h_1 h_2} + \frac{e^{2Ah_1}}{h_1(h_1 + h_2)} + \frac{e^{-2Ah_2}}{h_2(h_1 + h_2)}\right]$$

$$- Ae^{2Ax}\left[\frac{h_1 - h_2}{h_1 h_2} + \frac{h_2}{h_1(h_1 + h_2)} e^{2Ah_1} - \frac{h_1}{h_2(h_1 + h_2)} e^{-2Ah_2}\right].$$

Hence

$$(7.33) \quad l_h[\psi] \geq \frac{e^{2Ax}}{h_1 h_2(h_1 + h_2)} [-2(h_1 + h_2) + 2h_2 e^{2Ah_1} + 2h_1 e^{-2Ah_2}$$

$$- A(h_1^2 - h_2^2) - Ah_2^2 e^{2Ah_1} + Ah_1^2 e^{-2Ah_2}]$$

$$= \frac{e^{2Ax}}{h_1 h_2(h_1 + h_2)} [2h_1(e^{-2Ah_2} - 1) + 2h_2(e^{2Ah_1} - 1)$$

$$+ Ah_1^2(e^{-2Ah_2} - 1) - Ah_2^2(e^{2Ah_1} - 1)]$$

$$= \frac{e^{2Ax}}{h_1 h_2(h_1 + h_2)} [h_1(e^{-2Ah_2} - 1)(2 + Ah_1)$$

$$+ h_2(e^{2Ah_1} - 1)(2 - Ah_2)].$$

Now, since

$$(7.34) \qquad e^{2Ah_1} = 1 + 2Ah_1 + 2A^2h_1^2 + \epsilon_1, \qquad \text{where } \epsilon_1 = O(h_1^3)$$

$$(7.35) \qquad e^{-2Ah_2} = 1 - 2Ah_2 + 2A^2h_2^2 + \epsilon_2, \qquad \text{where } \epsilon_2 = O(h_2^3),$$

choose h sufficiently small so that, in addition to (7.15),

$$(7.36) \qquad \left|\frac{\epsilon_1(2 - Ah_2)}{h_1(h_1 + h_2)}\right| < \frac{A^2}{2}$$

$$(7.37) \qquad \left|\frac{\epsilon_2(2 + Ah_1)}{h_2(h_1 + h_2)}\right| < \frac{A^2}{2}.$$

Then, substitution of (7.34) and (7.35) into (7.33) implies, with the aid of (7.36) and (7.37), that

(7.38)

$$
\begin{aligned}
l_h[\psi] &\geq \frac{e^{2Ax}}{h_1 h_2 (h_1 + h_2)} [h_1(-2Ah_2 + 2A^2 h_2^2 + \epsilon_2)(2 + Ah_1) \\
&\quad + h_2(2Ah_1 + 2A^2 h_1^2 + \epsilon_1)(2 - Ah_2)] \\
&= \frac{e^{2Ax}}{h_1 h_2 (h_1 + h_2)} [h_1(2Ah_2)(Ah_2 - 1)(2 + Ah_1) \\
&\quad + h_1 \epsilon_2(2 + Ah_1) + h_2(2Ah_1)(1 + Ah_1)(2 - Ah_2) \\
&\quad + h_2 \epsilon_1(2 - Ah_2)] \\
&= \frac{e^{2Ax}}{h_1 h_2 (h_1 + h_2)} [2Ah_1 h_2(Ah_2 + Ah_1) + \epsilon_2 h_1(2 + Ah_1) \\
&\quad + \epsilon_1 h_2(2 - Ah_2)] \\
&= \frac{e^{2Ax}}{h_1 h_2 (h_1 + h_2)} [2A^2 h_1 h_2(h_1 + h_2) + \epsilon_2 h_1(2 + Ah_1) + \epsilon_1 h_2(2 - Ah_2)] \\
&= 2A^2 e^{2Ax} + \frac{\epsilon_2 e^{2Ax}(2 + Ah_1)}{h_2(h_1 + h_2)} + \frac{\epsilon_1 e^{2Ax}(2 - Ah_2)}{h_1(h_1 + h_2)} \\
&\geq A^2 e^{2Ax}.
\end{aligned}
$$

Also, since

(7.39)
$$
\max_G \psi \leq e^{2Ad},
$$

it follows that for h in the range described above (7.29) is valid, since

(7.40)
$$
l_h[\psi] \geq A^2 e^{2Ax} \geq A^2 > 0,
$$

and (7.30) is valid with

(7.41)
$$
C = \frac{e^{2Ad}}{A^2}.
$$

The fundamental inequality is now established in the following theorem.

Theorem 7.1

Let v be any function defined on G_h. Then

(7.42)
$$
\max_{R_h} |v| \leq C \max_{R_h} |l_h[v]| + \max_{S_h} |v|,
$$

where max $|l_h[v]|$ is taken over all $(x,y,z) \in R_h$ for any fixed t, p, q, and r; where h is restricted to those values described in Lemma 7.4; and where C is given by (7.41).

Proof:

Let $\psi = e^{2Ax}$. Then, for each fixed t, p, q and r

$$\psi_i = \sum_{s=1}^{m} \tilde{G}^{is} l_h[\psi_s] + \sum_{j=1}^{n} \tilde{\Gamma}^{ij}\psi_{j+m}, \qquad i = 1, 2, \cdots, m.$$

But $\psi_i \geq 0$, so that for each $i = 1, 2, \cdots, m$

$$\sum_{s=1}^{m} |\tilde{G}^{is}|\, l_h[\psi_s] \leq \sum_{j=1}^{n} \tilde{\Gamma}^{ij}\psi_{j+m}.$$

Also, for each $i = 1, 2, \cdots, m$

(7.43)
$$\max_i \sum_{j=1}^{n} |\tilde{\Gamma}^{ij}| \leq 1,$$

so that

$$\{\min_{R_h} l_h[\psi_s]\} \sum_{s=1}^{m} |\tilde{G}^{is}| \leq \max_{S_h} \psi.$$

Thus, for each $i = 1, 2, \cdots, m$,

(7.44)
$$\sum_{s=1}^{m} |\tilde{G}^{is}| \leq C.$$

Hence (7.42) follows readily from (7.22), (7.23), (7.25), and (7.44).

7.5. INEQUALITIES FOR NONLINEAR DIFFERENCE EQUATIONS

At $(x,y,z) \in R$, define the nonlinear operator L for all $v \in C^2(R)$ by
$$L[v(x,y,z)] = \Delta[v(x,y,z)] - F(x,y,z,v(x,y,z), v_x(x,y,z), v_y(x,y,z), v_z(x,y,z)).$$
At $(x,y,z) \in R_h$, define the nonlinear operator L_h for all v defined on G_h by

(7.45) $L_h[v(x,y,z)] = \Delta_h[v(x,y,z)]$
$$- F(x,y,z,v(x,y,z), v_{x,h}(x,y,z), v_{y,h}(x,y,z), v_{z,h}(x,y,z)).$$

Theorem 7.2

Let $v^{(1)}$, $v^{(2)}$ be any two functions defined on G_h. Then if h satisfies (7.15), (7.36), and (7.37), it follows that

(7.46) $\max_{R_h} |v^{(1)} - v^{(2)}| \leq C \max_{R_h} |L_h[v^{(1)}] - L_h[v^{(2)}]| + \max_{S_h} |v^{(1)} - v^{(2)}|,$

where C is given by (7.41).

Proof:

Set

(7.47) $$v(x,y,z) = v^{(1)}(x,y,z) - v^{(2)}(x,y,z).$$

Now fix a point $(\bar{x},\bar{y},\bar{z}) \in R_h$. Then

$$L_h[v^{(1)}(\bar{x},\bar{y},\bar{z})] - L_h[v^{(2)}(\bar{x},\bar{y},\bar{z})]$$
$$= \Delta_h[v^{(1)}(\bar{x},\bar{y},\bar{z})] - \Delta_h[v^{(2)}(\bar{x},\bar{y},\bar{z})]$$
$$- \{F(\bar{x},\bar{y},\bar{z}, v^{(1)}(\bar{x},\bar{y},\bar{z}), v^{(1)}_{x,h}(\bar{x},\bar{y},\bar{z}), v^{(1)}_{y,h}(\bar{x},\bar{y},\bar{z}), v^{(1)}_{z,h}(\bar{x},\bar{y},\bar{z}))$$
$$- F(\bar{x},\bar{y},\bar{z}, v^{(2)}(\bar{x},\bar{y},\bar{z}), v^{(2)}_{x,h}(\bar{x},\bar{y},\bar{z}), v^{(2)}_{y,h}(\bar{x},\bar{y},\bar{z}), v^{(2)}_{z,h}(\bar{x},\bar{y},\bar{z}))\}$$
$$= \Delta_h[v^{(1)}(\bar{x},\bar{y},\bar{z}) - v^{(2)}(\bar{x},\bar{y},\bar{z})]$$
$$- \{[v^{(1)}(\bar{x},\bar{y},\bar{z}) - v^{(2)}(\bar{x},\bar{y},\bar{z})]F_t(\bar{x},\bar{y},\bar{z},\bar{t},\bar{p},\bar{q},\bar{r})$$
$$+ [v^{(1)}_{x,h}(\bar{x},\bar{y},\bar{z}) - v^{(2)}_{x,h}(\bar{x},\bar{y},\bar{z})]F_p(\bar{x},\bar{y},\bar{z},\bar{t},\bar{p},\bar{q},\bar{r})$$
$$+ [v^{(1)}_{y,h}(\bar{x},\bar{y},\bar{z}) - v^{(2)}_{y,h}(\bar{x},\bar{y},\bar{z})]F_q(\bar{x},\bar{y},\bar{z},\bar{t},\bar{p},\bar{q},\bar{r})$$
$$+ [v^{(1)}_{z,h}(\bar{x},\bar{y},\bar{z}) - v^{(2)}_{z,h}(\bar{x},\bar{y},\bar{z})]F_r(\bar{x},\bar{y},\bar{z},\bar{t},\bar{p},\bar{q},\bar{r})\},$$

where, by the Mean Value Theorem, $\bar{t}$ lies between $v^{(1)}(\bar{x},\bar{y},\bar{z})$ and $v^{(2)}(\bar{x},\bar{y},\bar{z})$; $\bar{p}$ lies between $v^{(1)}_{x,h}(\bar{x},\bar{y},\bar{z})$ and $v^{(2)}_{x,h}(\bar{x},\bar{y},\bar{z})$; $\bar{q}$ lies between $v^{(1)}_{y,h}(\bar{x},\bar{y},\bar{z})$ and $v^{(2)}_{y,h}(\bar{x},\bar{y},\bar{z})$; $\bar{r}$ lies between $v^{(1)}_{z,h}(\bar{x},\bar{y},\bar{z})$ and $v^{(2)}_{z,h}(\bar{x},\bar{y},\bar{z})$.

Thus, from (7.12) and (7.47), with

(7.48)
$$\alpha^{(1)}(x,y,z,\bar{t},\bar{p},\bar{q},\bar{r}) = -F_p(x,y,z,\bar{t},\bar{p},\bar{q},\bar{r})$$
$$\alpha^{(2)}(x,y,z,\bar{t},\bar{p},\bar{q},\bar{r}) = -F_q(x,y,z,\bar{t},\bar{p},\bar{q},\bar{r})$$
$$\alpha^{(3)}(x,y,z,\bar{t},\bar{p},\bar{q},\bar{r}) = -F_r(x,y,z,\bar{t},\bar{p},\bar{q},\bar{r})$$
$$\gamma(x,y,z,\bar{t},\bar{p},\bar{q},\bar{r}) = F_t(x,y,z,\bar{t},\bar{p},\bar{q},\bar{r}),$$

one has that, for $t = \bar{t}, p = \bar{p}, q = \bar{q}, r = \bar{r}$,

(7.49) $$l_h[v(\bar{x},\bar{y},\bar{z})] = l_h[v^{(1)}(\bar{x},\bar{y},\bar{z}) - v^{(2)}(\bar{x},\bar{y},\bar{z})]$$
$$= L_h[v^{(1)}(\bar{x},\bar{y},\bar{z})] - L_h[v^{(2)}(\bar{x},\bar{y},\bar{z})].$$

Finally, as $(\bar{x},\bar{y},\bar{z})$ is allowed to vary over R_h, (7.46) follows directly from (7.42), (7.47), and (7.49).

Corollary 1

If $C_2 = \max\limits_{G} |F(x,y,z,0,0,0,0)|$, then for any function $v(x,y,z)$

(7.50) $$\max\limits_{R_h} |v| \le CC_2 + C \max\limits_{R_h} |L_h[v]| + \max\limits_{S_h} |v|.$$

Proof:
   The proof follows by setting $v \equiv v^{(1)}$, $v^{(2)} \equiv 0$, and applying (7.46).

Corollary 2
   If v is a solution of the numerical method described in Section (7.3), then

(7.51) $$\max_{R_h} |v| \leq K = CC_2 + \max_{S_h} |\phi|.$$

Proof:
   The proof is a direct consequence of (7.50), since $L_h[v] = 0$ and $v \equiv \phi$ on S_h.

7.6. EXISTENCE AND UNIQUENESS OF THE NUMERICAL SOLUTION

Lemma 7.5
   For all h that imply the validity of (7.15), (7.36), and (7.37), there exists *at most* one numerical solution of the numerical method prescribed in Section 7.3.

Proof:
   Suppose $v^{(1)}$ and $v^{(2)}$ are two numerical solutions. Then, from (7.46),
$$\max_{R_h} |v^{(1)} - v^{(2)}| = 0,$$
from which the theorem follows immediately.

Lemma 7.6
   For all h which imply the validity of (7.15), (7.36), and (7.37), there exists *at least* one numerical solution.

Proof:
   Let B^{is} and $\mathring{B}^{is}$ be the Green's matrix and Green's boundary matrix, respectively, for Δ_h and G_h. For the real parameter ω, $0 \leq \omega \leq 1$, define the family of *continuous* transformations $\vec{u}^* = T_\omega(\vec{u})$ in the m-dimensional $(u_1, u_2, \cdots, u_m)$ space by the equations

(7.52) $$u_i^* = u_i - \omega \sum_{s=1}^{m} B^{is} F(x_s, y_s, z_s, u_s, u_{x,h}, u_{y,h}, u_{z,h})$$

$$- \sum_{j=1}^{n} \mathring{B}^{ij} \phi_{j+m}, \qquad i = 1, 2, \cdots, m,$$

where the partial differences in (7.52) are evaluated at the point of R_h numbered s. A point $\vec{u} = (u_1, \cdots, u_m)$ taken by the transformation into the zero vector is a solution of the system

$$(7.53) \quad \Delta_h[u_i] - \omega F\{x_i, y_i, z_i, u_i, u_{x,h}, u_{y,h}, u_{z,h}\} = 0, \qquad i = 1, 2, \cdots, m,$$

$$u_i = \phi_i, \qquad i = m+1, \cdots, m+n,$$

where the partial differences in (7.53) are evaluated at the point of R_h numbered i.

Let $\overline{W}$ denote the set of vectors $\vec{u}$ whose coordinates satisfy $u_1^2 + u_2^2 + \cdots + u_m^2 \leq mK^2 + 1$, where K is given by (7.51). Now let $\vec{u}' = (u_1', u_2', \cdots, u_m')$ be a boundary point of $\overline{W}$, i.e., let

$$(7.54) \qquad (u_1')^2 + (u_2')^2 + \cdots + (u_m')^2 = mK^2 + 1.$$

Suppose, for fixed ω, $T_\omega(\vec{u}') = \vec{0}$. Then $\vec{u}'$ would be a numerical solution so that, by (7.51),

$$(7.55) \qquad \max_{R_h} (|u_1'|, |u_2'|, \cdots, |u_m'|) \leq K.$$

But, by (7.54),

$$\max_{R_h} (|u_1'|, |u_2'|, \cdots, |u_m'|) > K.$$

By contradiction, then, *no* point of the boundary of $\overline{W}$ maps into the origin. However, C is independent of ω and for $0 \leq \omega \leq 1$, the same C_2 in (7.51) is valid, so that the above contradiction follows for all ω in the range $0 \leq \omega \leq 1$. Thus, the degree of the map T_ω of $\overline{W}$ at the origin—that is, the m-dimensional solid angle under which the image of the boundary of $\overline{W}$ under T_ω is seen from the origin, divided by the measure of the m-dimensional unit sphere—is well defined (consult, e.g., Bers [2]). However, T_ω depends continuously on ω, so that this degree is independent of ω. For $\omega = 0$, the map T_0 is a translation which takes $\vec{u}^0 = (u_1^0, u_2^0, \cdots, u_m^0)$ with $u_i^0 = \sum_{j=1}^{n} \hat{B}^{ij} \phi_{j+m}$ of $\overline{W}$ into the origin. Hence, the degree is 1. Thus, for $\omega = 1$, at least one point $\vec{u}$ of $\overline{W}$ satisfies $T_1(\vec{u}) = \vec{0}$, and the lemma is proved.

Theorem 7.3

For all h that imply the validity of (7.15), (7.36), and (7.37), the numerical method of Section 7.3 has a unique solution.

Proof:

The proof is a direct consequence of Lemmas 7.5 and 7.6.

7.7. CONVERGENCE

Consider finally the question of convergence of the numerical to the analytical solution of the boundary value problem under consideration.

Theorem 7.4

If the analytical solution u of the boundary value problem of Definition 7.2 is of class $C^2(G)$, then $U \to u$ as $h \to 0$.

Proof:

Note first that at $(x,y,z) \in R_h$

$$(7.56) \quad \Delta_h u - \Delta u = \frac{h_1}{h_1 + h_2} u_{xx}(\xi_1, y, z) + \frac{h_2}{h_1 + h_2} u_{xx}(\xi_2, y, z)$$

$$+ \frac{h_3}{h_3 + h_4} u_{yy}(x, \xi_3, z) + \frac{h_4}{h_3 + h_4} u_{yy}(x, \xi_4, z)$$

$$+ \frac{h_5}{h_5 + h_6} u_{zz}(x, y, \xi_5) + \frac{h_6}{h_5 + h_6} u_{zz}(x, y, \xi_6) - u_{xx} - u_{yy},$$

where

$$x < \xi_1 < x + h_1, \quad y < \xi_3 < y + h_3, \quad z < \xi_5 < z + h_5,$$
$$x - h_2 < \xi_2 < x, \quad y - h_4 < \xi_4 < y, \quad z - h_6 < \xi_6 < z.$$

By the continuity of u_{xx}, u_{yy}, and u_{zz}, let

$$u_{xx}(\xi_i, y, z) = u_{xx} + \epsilon_i, \qquad i = 1, 2$$
$$u_{yy}(x, \xi_i, z) = u_{yy} + \epsilon_i, \qquad i = 3, 4$$
$$u_{zz}(x, y, \xi_i) = u_{zz} + \epsilon_i, \qquad i = 5, 6.$$

Then (7.56) reduces to

$$(7.57) \qquad \Delta_h u - \Delta u = \frac{\epsilon_1 h_1}{h_1 + h_2} + \frac{\epsilon_2 h_2}{h_1 + h_2} + \frac{\epsilon_3 h_3}{h_3 + h_4}$$

$$+ \frac{\epsilon_4 h_4}{h_3 + h_4} + \frac{\epsilon_5 h_5}{h_5 + h_6} + \frac{\epsilon_6 h_6}{h_5 + h_6}.$$

By the uniform continuity of u_{xx}, u_{yy}, and u_{zz} on G, it follows from (7.57) that independently of (x,y,z)

$$(7.58) \qquad |\Delta_h u - \Delta u| < \epsilon$$

for any given ϵ and for all sufficiently small h.

In a similar fashion, it follows that independently of (x,y,z)

$$|u_{x,h} - u_x| < \epsilon$$

(7.59)
$$|u_{y,h} - u_y| < \epsilon$$

$$|u_{z,h} - u_z| < \epsilon$$

for any given ϵ and for all sufficiently small h.

Hence, from (7.46)

$$\max_{R_h} |U - u|$$

$$\leq C\{\max_{R_h} |L_h[U] - L_h[u]|\} + \max_{S_h} |U - u|$$

$$= C \max_{R_h} |L_h[u] - L[u]|$$

$$\leq C \max_{R_h} [|\Delta_h u - \Delta u| + |F(x,y,z,u,u_{x,h},u_{y,h},u_{z,h}) - F(x,y,z,u,u_x,u_y,u_z)|]$$

$$\leq C \max_{R_h} [|\Delta_h u - \Delta u| + A|u_{x,h} - u_x| + A|u_{y,h} - u_y| + A|u_{z,h} - u_z|]$$

$$< \epsilon C(1 + 3A),$$

from which the theorem follows readily.

7.8. EXAMPLES

The following two examples are presented to indicate the ease with which one may often apply the numerical method of Section 7.3 to problems of real physical significance. Also, they indicate what has been found from experience, but for which no mathematical basis exists, that is, that the Generalized Newton's Method is remarkably faster than the Nonlinear Liebmann Iteration Method.

Example 1. In E^3, let G be the spherical sector of Example 1, Section 6.4. Let F in (7.3) be $F \equiv e^u$ (see Frank and von Mises [1] for the physical significance of this problem). Set $(\bar{x},\bar{y},\bar{z}) = (0,0,0)$, $h = .1$ and let $\phi = x + 2y + z^2$. R_h contains 410 points. The resulting nonlinear equations were solved by the Generalized Newton's Method (see Appendix) with $\omega = 1.8$ and zero initial vector. The running time was 2 minutes and 33 seconds. Selected, but typical, results are recorded under U in Table 7.1.

TABLE 7.1

x	y	z	U	x	y	z	U
.1	.1	.1	.33379803	.4	.1	.3	.77843093
.1	.2	.4	.73417575	.4	.2	.1	.88700006
.1	.3	.5	1.04443022	.4	.3	.3	1.28020294
.1	.4	.3	1.08918215	.4	.3	.7	1.61368477
.1	.5	.2	1.23012008	.4	.4	.4	1.58080909
.1	.6	.4	1.57000816	.4	.5	.7	1.95821289
.1	.7	.4	1.75731038	.4	.6	.3	1.89143826
.1	.8	.2	1.81786813	.4	.7	.5	2.12651462
.1	.9	.4	2.06963333	.4	.8	.2	2.13369786
.2	.1	.5	.72353422	.5	.1	.4	.95402334
.2	.2	.3	.80203491	.5	.2	.3	1.14019526
.2	.2	.9	1.44682719	.5	.3	.2	1.29857485
.2	.3	.9	1.63582348	.5	.4	.4	1.66722297
.2	.4	.8	1.71152454	.5	.5	.7	1.99755020
.2	.5	.8	1.87751902	.5	.7	.2	2.06195601
.2	.7	.1	1.70257965	.6	.1	.3	.97486870
.2	.8	.1	1.88993511	.6	.2	.6	1.45675948
.3	.1	.1	.55309066	.6	.4	.3	1.66927338
.3	.1	.6	.94374260	.6	.5	.6	1.98270586
.3	.2	.7	1.30608156	.6	.7	.3	2.13505733
.3	.3	.5	1.33513052	.7	.1	.7	1.39334550
.3	.4	.4	1.47053424	.7	.4	.2	1.59571747
.3	.5	.2	1.51616497	.7	.5	.3	1.89236582
.3	.6	.3	1.79105773	.8	.1	.2	1.09268284
.3	.6	.4	1.85851258	.8	.2	.5	1.48122715
.3	.7	.4	2.01526321	.8	.4	.3	1.75110486
.3	.9	.1	2.14891247	.9	.1	.3	1.21296598

Example 2. Nonlinear Liebmann Iteration (see Appendix) was applied to Example 1. Newton's method was applied to solve each equation. The running time was 4 minutes, 20 seconds. The results agreed with those of Example 1 to at least 8 decimal places.

7.9. A SUBSONIC FLOW PROBLEM

Nonlinear elliptic equations other than mildly nonlinear ones are, in general, very difficult to treat numerically. However, the equation

(7.60) $$\Delta u = u^2,$$

which is of interest in gas dynamics (Pohozaev [1], Wise and Ablow [1]), is an exception, and an associated Dirichlet problem is formulated in three dimensions as follows. Let R be bounded, homeomorphic to the interior of the unit sphere and have boundary S. Set $G = R \cup S$. Assume $\phi(x,y,z)$ is continuous and *nonnegative* on S. Then find a function $u(x,y,z) \in C^2(R)$ which possesses the following four properties:

(a) u is a solution of (7.60) on R,

(b) $u \equiv \phi$ on S,

(c) u is continuous on G,

(d) u is nonnegative on G.

Under rather general assumptions on the structure of S, the existence and uniqueness of the solution $u(x,y,z)$ of the above problem was established by Pohozaev [1], and it is only with such problems that we shall be concerned. And because, in general, the solution cannot be given in closed form, we shall consider a method for approximating it. The numerical method will be, essentially, a discretized form of the Newtonian iteration procedure:

$$(7.61) \quad \begin{cases} u^{(k)} \equiv \phi, & (x,y,z) \in S, \quad k = 0, 1, 2, \cdots \\ \Delta u^{(0)} = 0, & (x,y,z) \in R \\ \Delta u^{(k)} - 2u^{(k-1)}u^{(k)} = -[u^{(k-1)}]^2, & (x,y,z) \in R, \quad k = 1, 2, \cdots, \end{cases}$$

deduced by Pohozaev to show the existence and uniqueness of $u(x,y,z)$.

Note, with regard to (7.61), that if $u^{(k-1)}$ in the iteration formula is considered known and $u^{(k)}$ is considered unknown, then the result is a linear equation in $u^{(k)}$ of the form

$$(7.62) \qquad\qquad \Delta u - Au = B, \qquad A, B \text{ constants,}$$

and, from the discussions in Sections 4.1 and 4.2, it follows readily that at a point (x,y,z) of the type shown in Figure 6.1 that

$$\left(-A - \frac{2}{h_1 h_2} - \frac{2}{h_3 h_4} - \frac{2}{h_5 h_6}\right) u_0 + \frac{2}{h_1(h_1 + h_2)} u_1 + \frac{2}{h_2(h_1 + h_2)} u_2$$
$$+ \frac{2}{h_3(h_3 + h_4)} u_3 + \frac{2}{h_4(h_3 + h_4)} u_4$$
$$+ \frac{2}{h_5(h_5 + h_6)} u_5 + \frac{2}{h_6(h_5 + h_6)} u_6 = B$$

is a difference analogue of (7.62).

The numerical method is now formulated as follows.

Numerical Method

Step 1. Construct R_h and S_h as described in Section 6.2 and number the points as there indicated.

Step 2. For the Dirichlet Problem for

$$\Delta u = 0, \qquad (x,y,z) \in R$$

$$u = \phi, \qquad (x,y,z) \in S,$$

let $U_i^{(0)}$, $i = 1, 2, \cdots, m + n$, be the numerical solution generated by the method of Section 6.2.

Step 3. Construct $U_i^{(k)}$ in terms of $U_i^{(k-1)}$, $k = 1, 2, \cdots$, by $U_i^{(k)} \equiv \phi_i$ on S_h, while, at each point of R_h, as shown in Figure 6.1, $U_i^{(k)}$ satisfies the difference equation

$$(7.63) \quad \left[-2U_0^{(k-1)} - \frac{2}{h_1 h_2} - \frac{2}{h_3 h_4} - \frac{2}{h_5 h_6} \right] U_0^{(k)} + \frac{2}{h_1(h_1 + h_2)} U_1^{(k)}$$

$$+ \frac{2}{h_2(h_1 + h_2)} U_2^{(k)} + \frac{2}{h_3(h_3 + h_4)} U_3^{(k)} + \frac{2}{h_4(h_3 + h_4)} U_4^{(k)}$$

$$+ \frac{2}{h_5(h_5 + h_6)} U_5^{(k)} + \frac{2}{h_6(h_5 + h_6)} U_6^{(k)} = -[U_0^{(k-1)}]^2.$$

Step 4. The numerical procedure terminates when $U_i^{(k)} = U_i^{(k-1)}$, $i = 1, 2, \cdots, m + n$, and this final $U_i^{(k)}$ is defined to be the numerical solution.

Of course, as is usual in the linear case, the existence and uniqueness of each $U_i^{(k)}$, $k = 0, 1, \cdots$, follows readily from Lemma 2.1. Attention therefore will be directed to questions of convergence, for which the analytical methods of Pohozaev will be discretized.

Consider first the boundary value problem defined on $G_h = R_h \cup S_h$ by

$$(7.64) \quad \Delta_h U_i = (U_i)^2, \qquad (x,y,z) \in R_h, \quad i = 1, 2, \cdots, m,$$

$$(7.65) \quad U_i = \phi_i, \qquad (x,y,z) \in S_h, \quad i = m + 1, \cdots, m + n,$$

$$(7.66) \quad U_i \geq 0, \qquad (x,y,z) \in G_h, \quad i = 1, 2, \cdots, m + n.$$

Lemma 7.7

If the problem defined by (7.64)–(7.66) on $G_h = R_h \cup S_h$ has a solution, then that solution is unique.

Proof:

Assume there exist two solutions $U_{i,1}$, $U_{i,2}$, $i = 1, 2, \cdots, m + n$. Let $W_i = U_{i,1} - U_{i,2}$. Then, on R_h

(7.67)
$$\Delta_h W_i = (U_{i,1})^2 - (U_{i,2})^2 = (U_{i,1} + U_{i,2})W_i, \qquad i = 1, 2, \cdots, m,$$

while, on S_h,

(7.68) $$W_i = 0, \qquad i = m + 1, m + 2, \cdots, m + n.$$

Since $U_{i,1} + U_{i,2} \geq 0$, it follows from Lemma 2.1, as applied to (7.67), that W_i possesses a weak max–min property on G_h. Hence, by (7.68), one has that on G_h

$$W_i \leq 0, \qquad i = 1, 2, \cdots, m + n.$$

Thus,

$$U_{i,1} \leq U_{i,2}, \qquad i = 1, 2, \cdots, m + n.$$

But, by reversing the roles of $U_{i,1}$ and $U_{i,2}$, it follows that

$$U_{i,1} \geq U_{i,2}, \qquad i = 1, 2, \cdots, m + n.$$

Hence, $U_{i,1} = U_{i,2}$ on G_h and the lemma is proved.

Lemma 7.8

On $G_h = R_h \cup S_h$, let $V_i \geq 0$, $i = 1, 2, \cdots, m + n$. Let U_i, $i = 1, 2, \cdots, m + n$, be the unique function on G_h which satisfies both

(7.69) $$\Delta_h U_i - 2V_i U_i = -(V_i)^2, \qquad (x,y,z) \in R_h, \quad i = 1, 2, \cdots, m,$$

and

(7.70) $$U_i = \phi_i, \qquad (x,y,z) \in S_h,$$

$$i = m + 1, m + 2, \cdots, m + n.$$

Then on G_h

(7.71) $$U_i \geq 0, \qquad (x,y,z) \in G_h, \quad i = 1, 2, \cdots, m + n.$$

Proof:

If $\min\limits_{G_h} U_i$ occurs on S_h, then the lemma is valid since $\phi \geq 0$. Suppose then that at $(\bar{x},\bar{y},\bar{z}) \in R_h$, $U(\bar{x},\bar{y},\bar{z}) = \min\limits_{G_h} U_i = m$, and that $U_i \neq m$ on S_h.

Case 1. Suppose $V(\bar{x},\bar{y},\bar{z}) \neq 0$. Then $V(\bar{x},\bar{y},\bar{z}) > 0$. Moreover, since $U(\bar{x},\bar{y},\bar{z})$ is minimal, then

$$U(\bar{x},\bar{y},\bar{z}) \leq \min [U(\bar{x} + h_1, \bar{y}, \bar{z}), U(\bar{x} - h_2, \bar{y}, \bar{z}), U(\bar{x}, \bar{y} + h_3, \bar{z}),$$
$$U(\bar{x}, \bar{y} - h_4, \bar{z}), U(\bar{x}, \bar{y}, \bar{z} + h_5), U(\bar{x}, \bar{y}, \bar{z} - h_6)],$$

so that

$$\Delta_h U(\bar{x}, \bar{y}, \bar{z}) \geq 0.$$

Thus, from (7.69), it follows that

$$2V(\bar{x},\bar{y},\bar{z})U(\bar{x},\bar{y},\bar{z}) = [V(\bar{x},\bar{y},\bar{z})]^2 + [\Delta_h U(\bar{x},\bar{y},\bar{z})] \geq [V(\bar{x},\bar{y},\bar{z})]^2.$$

Since $V(\bar{x},\bar{y},\bar{z}) \neq 0$, this last inequality implies

$$U(\bar{x},\bar{y},\bar{z}) \geq \tfrac{1}{2}V(\bar{x},\bar{y},\bar{z}) > 0.$$

Case 2. Suppose $V(\bar{x},\bar{y},\bar{z}) = 0$. Then $\Delta_h U(\bar{x},\bar{y},\bar{z}) = 0$ and (7.71) follows from the strong max–min property.

Cases 1 and 2, then, imply the validity of (7.71) and the lemma is proved.

Lemma 7.9

Let $U_i^{(k)}$, where for each fixed $k = 0, 1, 2, \cdots$, the index i takes on the values $i = 1, 2, \cdots, m + n$, be defined by the iterative procedure of Steps 2 and 3 of the Numerical Method of this section. Then, for each fixed $k = 0, 1, 2, \cdots$,

$$(7.72) \qquad\qquad U_i^{(k)} \geq 0, \qquad i = 1, 2, \cdots, m + n.$$

Proof:

From the strong max–min property, the lemma is valid for $k = 0$. The proof is completed readily then by induction by applying Lemma 7.8, for by setting $U_i = U_i^{(k)}$ and $V_i = U_i^{(k-1)}$ in (7.69), there results

$$(7.73) \qquad\qquad \Delta_h U_i^{(k)} - 2U_i^{(k-1)}U_i^{(k)} = -[U_i^{(k-1)}]^2.$$

Theorem 7.5

With regard to the Numerical Method of this section, the functions $U_i^{(k)}$, $i = 1, 2, \cdots, m + n$, are monotone decreasing with k, beginning with $k = 1$. By (7.72) then $U_i^{(k)}$ converges to some $U_i, i = 1, 2, \cdots, m + n$, where U_i satisfies (7.64)–(7.66) on G_h.

Proof:

Let

(7.74) $$\omega_i^{(k+1)} = U_i^{(k+1)} - U_i^{(k)}, \qquad k \geq 0, \quad i = 1, 2, \cdots, m+n.$$

Then

(7.75) $$\Delta_h U_i^{(k+1)} - 2U_i^{(k)} U_i^{(k+1)} = - [U_i^{(k)}]^2,$$
$$k \geq 0, \quad i = 1, 2, \cdots, m+n,$$

and

(7.76) $$\Delta_h U_i^{(k)} - 2U_i^{(k-1)} U_i^{(k)} = -[U_i^{(k-1)}]^2,$$
$$k \geq 1, \ i = 1, 2, \cdots, m+n.$$

Subtracting (7.76) from (7.75) implies then that

$$\Delta_h \omega_i^{(k+1)} - 2U_i^{(k)} U_i^{(k+1)} = [U_i^{(k-1)}]^2 - 2U_i^{(k-1)} U_i^{(k)} - [U_i^{(k)}]^2.$$

Hence,

$$\Delta_h \omega_i^{(k+1)} - 2U_i^{(k)} U_i^{(k+1)} + 2[U_i^{(k)}]^2 = [U_i^{(k-1)}]^2 - 2U_i^{(k-1)} U_i^{(k)} + [U_i^{(k)}]^2,$$

or, equivalently,

(7.77) $$\Delta_h \omega_i^{(k+1)} - 2U_i^{(k)} \omega_i^{(k+1)} = [\omega_i^{(k)}]^2, \qquad k \geq 1, \quad i = 1, 2, \cdots, m+n.$$

However, (7.77) implies

$$\Delta_h \omega_i^{(k+1)} - 2U_i^{(k)} \omega_i^{(k+1)} \geq 0,$$

which by (7.72), the weak max–min property, and the fact that $\omega_i^{(k)} \equiv 0$ on S_h for all $k \geq 1$ implies that

$$\omega_i^{(k+1)} \leq 0, \qquad k \geq 1, \quad i = 1, 2, \cdots, m+n.$$

Thus, from (7.74),

$$U_i^{(k+1)} \leq U_i^{(k)}, \qquad k \geq 1, \quad i = 1, 2, \cdots, m+n,$$

from which the indicated monotonicity is established. The convergence of the sequence $U_i^{(k)}$ to U_i then follows from (7.72). The fact that U_i satisfies (7.64)–(7.66) on G_h follows because

$$\lim_{k \to \infty} \{\Delta_h U_i^{(k+1)} - 2U_i^{(k)} U_i^{(k+1)} + [U_i^{(k)}]^2\} \equiv \Delta_h U_i - [U_i]^2,$$

and the theorem is proved.

Note immediately that since calculations on a high speed computer are in terms of a fixed, finite number of digits, Theorem 7.5 implies that the

Numerical Method of this section will converge to within any given machine tolerance in a *finite* number of steps.

Next we establish conditions under which the numerical solution converges to the analytical solution.

Theorem 7.6

If $u \in C^2(G)$, then as $h \to 0$ the numerical solution $U_i = \lim_{k \to \infty} U_i^{(k)}$, $i = 1, 2, \cdots, m + n$, generated by the Numerical Method of this section converges to the analytical solution $u(x,y,z)$ of the given boundary value problem for (7.60).

Proof:

On G_h, set $E^{(i)} = U_i - u_i$, $i = 1, 2, \cdots, m + n$. Since $E^{(i)} = 0$ on S_h, we need only consider $E^{(i)}$ on R_h. Then, at $(x,y,z) \in R_h$ and numbered i, one has

$$\Delta_h E^{(i)} = U_i^2 - \Delta_h u_i.$$

But, since by assumption $u \in C^2(G)$, it follows from (7.57) and (7.58) that

(7.78) $$\Delta_h E^{(i)} = U_i^2 - \Delta u_i + \epsilon_i(x,y,z,h),$$

where, independently of (x,y,z), $\epsilon_i \to 0$ as $h \to 0$.

Now, from (7.78) one has

$$\begin{aligned} \Delta_h E^{(i)} &= U_i^2 - u_i^2 + \epsilon_i \\ &= (U_i + u_i)(U_i - u_i) + \epsilon_i \\ &= (U_i + u_i)E^{(i)} + \epsilon_i. \end{aligned}$$

Thus, (7.78) is equivalent to

(7.79) $$\Delta_h E^{(i)} - (U_i + u_i)E^{(i)} = \epsilon_i.$$

However, Pohozaev [1] showed that $u(x,y,z) \geq 0$ on G and, from (7.72), $U_i \geq 0$ on G_h. Hence, one can apply (7.42) to (7.79), so that

(7.80) $$\max_{R_h} |E^{(i)}| \leq C \max_{R_h} |\epsilon_i| + \max_{S_h} |E^{(i)}|.$$

Thus, the convergence as $h \to 0$ follows from (7.80), since $E^{(i)} = 0$ on S_h and, as $h \to 0$, $\epsilon_i \to 0$ uniformly on G_h. Hence, the theorem is proved.

Finally we note that the ideas of this section extend to other nonlinear problems (see Greenspan and Parter [1] and Parter [3]) and we give an example to demonstrate the feasibility of the present method.

TABLE 7.2

x	y	z	Approximate Solution	Exact Solution $u = \dfrac{126}{(x + 2y + 4z + 1)^2}$
.05	.05	.65	8.9609	8.9600
.05	.20	.40	13.5529	13.5447
.05	.50	.15	17.9539	17.9423
.05	.80	.45	6.3637	6.3629
.10	.25	.80	5.4700	5.4687
.10	.60	.40	8.2891	8.2840
.10	.90	.40	6.2226	6.2222
.15	.20	.35	14.5014	14.4786
.15	.50	.80	4.4028	4.4021
.20	.05	.60	9.2064	9.2038
.20	.25	.15	23.8766	23.8185
.20	.35	.90	4.1656	4.1653
.20	.80	.05	14.0043	14.0000
.25	.30	.15	21.0381	20.9913
.25	.60	.75	4.2423	4.2421
.25	.80	.50	5.3574	5.3566
.30	.15	.75	5.9570	5.9546
.30	.50	.80	4.1656	4.1653
.35	.10	.55	8.9659	8.9600
.35	.25	.80	4.9424	4.9407
.35	.45	.35	9.4732	9.4577
.40	.05	.45	11.5760	11.5702
.40	.10	.90	4.6600	4.6598
.40	.40	.35	9.7391	9.7222
.40	.90	.15	8.7261	8.7257
.45	.40	.20	13.5683	13.5447
.50	.05	.40	12.3112	12.3047
.50	.40	.65	5.2506	5.2478
.55	.10	.50	8.9657	8.9600
.55	.50	.35	8.0850	8.0756
.55	.80	.20	8.0763	8.0756
.60	.20	.75	5.0406	5.0400
.60	.70	.35	6.5091	6.5083
.65	.45	.15	12.7114	12.6984
.70	.25	.55	6.5113	6.5083
.75	.15	.60	6.3638	6.3628
.80	.15	.45	8.2873	8.2840
.85	.30	.20	11.9370	11.9290
.90	.25	.15	14.0071	14.0000
.95	.30	.05	16.6619	16.6612

Example. Let R be the set of points (x,y,z) whose coordinates satisfy $x > 0$, $y > 0$, $z > 0$, $x^2 + y^2 + z^2 < 1$. On S, the boundary of R, define $\phi(x,y,z) - 126(x + y + 4z + 1)^{-2}$. For $(\bar{x},\bar{y},\bar{z}) = (0,0,0)$ and $h = .05$, construct R_h and S_h. When applied, the Numerical Method of this section converged in 18 minutes, 43 seconds. Selected, but typical, results are recorded in Table 7.2.

7.10. RESEARCH PROBLEMS

Besides the variety of research problems which already have been presented either directly or as inferences from computing experiences consider finally some additional problems which are of more than routine interest and of more than routine difficulty.

Problem 1. The Plateau Problem.   In E^2, let R and S be defined as in Definition 1.3. Let $\phi(x,y)$ be defined and continuous on S. The **Plateau Problem** is that of finding a function u which has the following three properties:

(a) $u \in [C(R \cup S) \cap C^2(R)]$,
(b) $u \equiv \phi$ on S,
(c) u satisfies on R the nonlinear elliptic differential equation

$$(7.81) \qquad (1 + u_y^2)u_{xx} - 2u_x u_y u_{xy} + (1 + u_x^2)u_{yy} = 0.$$

For existence and uniqueness theorems for the Plateau Problem, consult Courant and Hilbert [1], Jesse Douglas [1], and Rado [1]. Note also that any solution of the Plateau Problem is called a **minimal surface.**
Neither finite difference nor variational methods have been successful in approximating minimal surfaces. However, the following combination technique has proved to be of great value thus far in all test problems run on the CDC 1604 (see Greenspan [12]).

Construct R_h and S_h as in Section 2.2. Assume that the grid thereby divides R into mutually disjoint subregions $R_1, R_2, \cdots, R_p$, whose respective boundaries are $S_1, S_2, \cdots, S_p$ and respective areas are A_1, $A_2, \cdots, A_p$. If possible, select in each S_i, $i = 1, 2, \cdots, p$, a point $(x_i, y_i) \in G_h$ at which one can approximate u_x and u_y, respectively, by finite difference expressions $u_{x,h,i}$ and $u_{y,h,i}$, which utilize only points of G_h.

Next reformulate the Plateau Problem as the variational problem (Courant and Hilbert [1]) of minimizing the functional

$$(7.82) \qquad J[u] = \iint\limits_{R \cup S} (1 + u_x^2 + u_y^2)^{1/2} \, dA.$$

Approximate $J[u]$ by

$$(7.83) \qquad J_p = \sum_{i=1}^{p} A_i [1 + (u_{x,h,i})^2 + (u_{y,h,i})^2]^{1/2},$$

which is a function only of $u_1, u_2, \cdots, u_m$. Minimize J_p by solving the system of m nonlinear algebraic equations

$$(7.84) \qquad \frac{\partial J_p}{\partial u_i} = 0, \qquad i = 1, 2, \cdots, m.$$

Let U_i, $i = 1, 2, \cdots, m$, be the solution of (7.84) and represent the desired approximation on R_h.

Show then that if the Plateau Problem has a unique solution u, then U_i exists and is unique, and $U_i \to u_i$ as $h \to 0$.

Problem 2. Devise an effective numerical method for approximating the solution to any of the following problems and prove pointwise convergence of the numerical to the analytical solution.

(a) The Exterior Dirichlet Problem (consult, e.g., Petrovsky [2], and for initial numerical efforts see Vlasov and Bakusinskii [1]).

(b) Elliptic Cauchy problems (consult, e.g., Garabedian [2], Miller [1], Newman [1], Sugai [1], Trytten [1]).

(c) Elliptic interface problems (for initial efforts in this direction consult Downing [1], Sheldon [2], and Squier [1]).

(d) Radiation problems associated with $\Delta u + k^2 u = 0$ (consult, e.g., Courant and Hilbert [1] and, for initial numerical efforts see Edwards [1.2].)

(e) Dirichlet type problems for the Monge-Ampere equation (consult, e.g., Courant and Hilbert [1]).

Problem 3. Give a mathematical theory to support the Generalized Newton's Method (see the Appendix).

Problem 4. Since continuous physical models are often inferred from discrete data and since discrete methods are now used extensively to approximate solutions of continuous problems, discuss the possibility and value of formulating only discrete models and of treating them directly.

EXERCISES

1. Let R be the set of points (x,y,z) whose coordinates satisfy $x^2 + y^2 + z^2 < 1$. Determine whether or not each of the following equations is mildly nonlinear on R.

(a) $u_{xx} + u_{yy} + u_{zz} = 1$.

(b) $u_{xx} + u_{yy} + u_{zz} = e^u$.

(c) $u_{xx} + u_{yy} + u_{zz} = e^x$.

(d) $u_{xx} + u_{yy} + u_{zz} = u^2$.

(e) $u_{xx} + u_{yy} + u_{zz} = u_x + u_y + e^u$.

(f) $u_{xx} + u_{yy} + u_{zz} = uu_x$.

(g) $u_{xx} + u_{yy} + u_{zz} = \sin u$.

(h) $u_{xx} + u_{yy} + u_{zz} = (u_x)^2$.

(i) $u_{xx} + u_{yy} + u_{zz} = u^3$.

(j) $u_{xx} + u_{yy} + u_{zz} = u^n$,

n a positive integer.

2. Show that if (7.3) is mildly nonlinear on G and if under the translation $x = x' + a$, $y = y' + b$, $z = z' + c$ the set G maps into G', then (7.3) transforms into an equation which is mildly nonlinear on G'.

3. In E^3 let R be the cubic region whose points (x,y,z) satisfy the relationships $1 < x < 2$, $1 < y < 2$, $1 < z < 2$. Let S be the boundary of R. For $F = u^3$ consider an associated mildly nonlinear Dirichlet problem with $\phi = \dfrac{\sqrt{2}}{y}$. Find the approximate solution described in Section 7.3 for each of the following.

(a) $(\bar{x},\bar{y},\bar{z}) = (1,1,1)$, $h = .4$.

(b) $(\bar{x},\bar{y},\bar{z}) = (1,1,1)$, $h = .3$.

(c) $(\bar{x},\bar{y},\bar{z}) = (1,1,1)$, $h = .2$.

(d) $(\bar{x},\bar{y},\bar{z}) = (1,1,1)$, $h = .1$.

(e) $(\bar{x},\bar{y},\bar{z}) = (1,1,1)$, $h = .01$.

Compare each approximate solution with the exact solution $u = \dfrac{\sqrt{2}}{y}$.

4. In E^3 let G be the spherical sector in the first octant bounded by the surfaces whose equations are $x = 0$, $y = 0$, $z = 0$, $x^2 + y^2 + z^2 = 1$. Let $F = e^u$ and consider an associated mildly nonlinear Dirichlet problem with $\phi = x + 2y + z^2$. Find the approximate solution as prescribed in Section 7.3 for each of the following.

(a) $(\bar{x},\bar{y},\bar{z}) = (0,0,0)$, $h = .3$.

(b) $(\bar{x},\bar{y},\bar{z}) = (0,0,0)$, $h = .2$.

(c) $(\bar{x},\bar{y},\bar{z}) = (0,0,0)$, $h = .05$.

When possible compare each approximate solution with the ones tabulated in Table 7.1. Also, in each case determine the number of points in R_h.

5. In E^3 let R be the cubic region whose points (x,y,z) satisfy the relationships $0 < x < 1$, $0 < y < 1$, $0 < z < 1$. Let S be the boundary of R and set

$(\bar{x},\bar{y},\bar{z}) = (0,0,0)$ and $h = .25$. By selecting $\psi(x,y,z)$ in accordance with the proof of Lemma 7.4, determine a numerical value $C(A,d)$ which satisfies (7.30). Consider then $v(x,y,z) = x + y - z$ and show by actually determining the values of the various quantities in (7.42) that that inequality is valid with the C just determined.

6. In E^3 let R be the cubic region described in Exercise 5. Set $(\bar{x},\bar{y},\bar{z}) = (0,0,0)$ and $h = .25$. Consider the numerical value $C(A,d)$ determined in Exercise 5. Then for $v(x,y,z) = x + y - z$ show by direct calculation of each of the quantities in (7.50) that that inequality is valid.

7. Let R be the set of points (x,y,z) whose coordinates satisfy $x > 0$, $y > 0$, $z > 0$, $x^2 + y^2 + z^2 < 1$. On S, the boundary of R, define $\phi(x,y,z) = 126(x + y + 4z + 1)^{-2}$. For $(\bar{x},\bar{y},\bar{z}) = (0,0,0)$ construct R_h and S_h for (a) $h = .3$, (b) $h = .1$, (c) $h = .025$. Apply the Numerical Method of Section 7.9 to approximate the solution of the associated boundary value problem for (7.60) and compare the results with the exact solution $u = 126(x + y + 4z + 1)^{-2}$.

8. Determine whether or not the discussion of Section 7.9 extends to the nonlinear equation

$$\Delta u = f(u); \quad f_u \geq 0$$

by first rewriting it in the form

$$\Delta u - [f_u(u)]u = f(u) - [f_u(u)]u$$

and then replacing the iteration formula in (7.61) with

$$\Delta u^{(n)} - [f_u(u^{(n-1)})]u^{(n)} = f(u^{(n-1)}) - [f_u(u^{(n-1)})]u^{(n-1)}.$$

9. Discuss the relative merits of the numerical method that results by replacing (7.63) with

$$\left[-\frac{2}{h_1 h_2} - \frac{2}{h_3 h_4} - \frac{2}{h_5 h_6} \right] U_0^{(k)} + \frac{2}{h_1(h_1 + h_2)} U_1^{(k)} + \frac{2}{h_2(h_1 + h_2)} U_2^{(k)}$$

$$+ \frac{2}{h_3(h_3 + h_4)} U_3^{(k)} + \frac{2}{h_4(h_3 + h_4)} U_4^{(k)} + \frac{2}{h_5(h_5 + h_6)} U_5^{(k)}$$

$$+ \frac{2}{h_6(h_5 + h_6)} U_6^{(k)} = [U_0^{(k-1)}]^2.$$

SOLUTION OF SYSTEMS
OF ALGEBRAIC
AND TRANSCENDENTAL EQUATIONS

A.1. LINEAR SYSTEMS

Any system of n linear algebraic equations

(A.1)
$$a_{11}x_1 + a_{12}x_2 + a_{13}x_3 + \cdots + a_{1n}x_n = b_1$$
$$a_{21}x_1 + a_{22}x_2 + a_{23}x_3 + \cdots + a_{2n}x_n = b_2$$
$$\cdot \qquad \cdot \qquad \cdot \qquad \qquad \cdot \qquad \cdot \quad , \qquad n \geq 2$$
$$a_{n1}x_1 + a_{n2}x_2 + a_{n3}x_3 + \cdots + a_{nn}x_n = b_n$$

in the unknowns $x_1, x_2, \cdots, x_n$ can be written in the form

(A.2)
$$Ax = b,$$

where $A = (a_{ij})$ is an $n \times n$ matrix and

$$x = \begin{pmatrix} x_1 \\ x_2 \\ \cdot \\ \cdot \\ \cdot \\ x_n \end{pmatrix}, \qquad b = \begin{pmatrix} b_1 \\ b_2 \\ \cdot \\ \cdot \\ \cdot \\ b_n \end{pmatrix}$$

are column vectors. It will be assumed that the elements of A and components of b are real numbers, and since interest will be directed toward systems which have unique solutions, it will be further assumed that A is nonsingular. Given then A and b, one can determine x, at least theoretically,

127

by such methods as Cramer's rule, Gauss elimination, the Gauss–Jordan method, matrix inversion, relaxation, the Crout method, the square root method, and the method of postmultiplication (see, e.g., Forsythe [1], Goodwin [1], Householder [1], Kunz [1]). If A possesses additional properties, like symmetry, positive definiteness, diagonal dominance, tridiagonal form or reducibility, then, accordingly, additional methods like the gradient method, the method of conjugate gradients, general iteration, Richardson's method, the Gauss–Seidel method, successive over-relaxation, and the Peaceman–Rachford method are also available (see, e.g., Goodwin [1], Hestenes and Stieffel [1], Householder [1], Varga [1], and D. Young [1, 2]).

With regard to the numerical solution of elliptic boundary value problems, the Gauss elimination, Gauss–Seidel, and successive over-relaxation methods have particular value and each will be described now in turn.

Gauss Elimination

With regard to system (A.1), select an equation in which the coefficient of x_1, say a_{k1}, is of maximum absolute value. Then add the multiple $-a_{j1}/a_{k1}$, $j \neq k$, of this kth equation to the jth equation for each of $j = 1, 2, \cdots, k-2, k-1, k+1, k+2, \cdots, n$. Set the kth equation aside and consider the remaining $(n-1)$ equations, which contain only the $(n-1)$ unknowns $x_2, x_3, \cdots, x_n$. Select from these an equation in which the coefficient of x_2 is of maximum absolute value and add suitable multiples of this equation to the remaining $(n-2)$ equations, so that in each resulting equation the coefficient of x_2 is zero. Set aside the equation whose x_2 coefficient is nonzero and consider the remaining $(n-2)$ equations in the $(n-2)$ unknowns $x_3, x_4, \cdots, x_n$. In an inductive fashion, apply the indicated elimination process until, in a finite number of steps, there results a system of equations of the form

$$
\begin{aligned}
c_{11}x_1 + c_{12}x_2 + c_{13}x_3 + \cdots + c_{1,n-1}x_{n-1} + c_{1n}x_n &= d_1 \\
c_{22}x_2 + c_{23}x_3 + \cdots + c_{2,n-1}x_{n-1} + c_{2n}x_n &= d_2 \\
c_{33}x_3 + \cdots + c_{3,n-1}x_{n-1} + c_{3n}x_n &= d_3 \\
\vdots \qquad \vdots \qquad \vdots \qquad \vdots \\
c_{n-1,n-1}x_{n-1} + c_{n-1,n}x_n &= d_{n-1} \\
c_{nn}x_n &= d_n,
\end{aligned}
$$

(A.3)

where $c_{ii} \neq 0$, $i = 1, 2, \cdots, n$. From the last equation of system (A.3), calculate x_n. Using this value of x_n, back-substitution into the next-to-the-last equation of system (A.3) readily yields x_{n-1}. Using then the values of x_n and x_{n-1}, back-substitution into the second-from-the-last equation of system (A.3) readily yields x_{n-2}. Proceeding then in the indicated fashion, one readily finds by back-substitution $x_{n-3}, x_{n-4}, \cdots, x_3, x_2, x_1$. The resulting vector x is, of course, also the unique solution of (A.1).

For special considerations in applying Gauss elimination on a digital computer, see Goldstine and von Neumann [1], Goodwin [1], and Kunz [1].

In contrast to Gauss elimination, which is *direct*, consider next the following ideas which will be useful in the development of *iteration* methods. For this purpose, however, it will be assumed in addition with regard to (1.1) that

(A.4) $$a_{ii} \neq 0, \qquad i = 1, 2, \cdots, n.$$

From (A.4), then, it follows that the matrix

(A.5) $$D = \begin{pmatrix} a_{11} & & & & O \\ & a_{22} & & & \\ & & \cdot & & \\ & & & \cdot & \\ & & & & \cdot \\ O & & & & a_{nn} \end{pmatrix}$$

is nonsingular and easily invertible. If one defines G by

(A.6) $$G = A - D,$$

then (A.6) and (A.2) imply

$$Dx = -Gx + b,$$

from which it follows that

(A.7) $$x = -D^{-1}Gx + D^{-1}b.$$

Since the unknown vector x occurs in two separate places in (A.7), substitution of $x^{(k+1)}$ for the x on the left-hand side of (A.7) and substitution of $x^{(k)}$ for the other x yields the iteration formula

(A.8) $$x^{(k+1)} = -D^{-1}Gx^{(k)} + D^{-1}b, \qquad k = 0, 1, 2, \cdots.$$

After an initial vector $x^{(0)}$ is given, (A.8) generates in an inductive fashion a sequence $x^{(i)}$, $i = 1, 2, \cdots$, which under favorable circumstances will converge to the solution of (A.7), and hence of (A.2).

Closer inspection of (A.8), however, reveals the possibility of developing a different iteration technique which might converge faster, if and when convergence for (A.8) were assured. Consider the actual computations involved in (A.8). Initially one substitutes vector $x^{(0)}$ into (A.8) and calculates, in turn, the components $x_1^{(1)}, x_2^{(1)}, \cdots, x_n^{(1)}$ of vector $x^{(1)}$. Suppose, however, that after calculating the component $x_1^{(1)}$, one were to substitute the vector

$$\begin{pmatrix} x_1^{(1)} \\ x_2^{(0)} \\ \cdot \\ \cdot \\ \cdot \\ x_n^{(0)} \end{pmatrix}$$

into (A.8) in order to calculate the component $x_2^{(1)}$; and then were to substitute the vector

$$\begin{pmatrix} x_1^{(1)} \\ x_2^{(1)} \\ x_3^{(0)} \\ \cdot \\ \cdot \\ x_n^{(0)} \end{pmatrix}$$

into (A.8) in order to calculate the component $x_3^{(1)}$, and so forth. Such a process for generating a vector $x^{(1)}$ uses new data as soon as it appears. In general, the iteration prescribed by (A.8) does *not* use new data as it appears and each component $x_1^{(k+1)}, x_2^{(k+1)}, \cdots, x_n^{(k+1)}$ of vector $x^{(k+1)}$ is computed in terms of the components $x_1^{(k)}, x_2^{(k)}, \cdots, x_n^{(k)}$ of vector $x^{(k)}$. The indicated modification uses the components of vector $x^{(k)}$ to compute only the first component of vector $x^{(k+1)}$, and then would use the vector

$$\begin{pmatrix} x_1^{(k+1)} \\ x_2^{(k)} \\ \cdot \\ \cdot \\ \cdot \\ x_n^{(k)} \end{pmatrix}$$

to compute component $x_2^{(k+1)}$, the vector

$$\begin{pmatrix} x_1^{(k+1)} \\ x_2^{(k+1)} \\ x_3^{(k)} \\ \cdot \\ \cdot \\ x_n^{(k)} \end{pmatrix}$$

to compute the component $x_3^{(k+1)}$, and so on, until each component of vector $x^{(k+1)}$ is generated. This technique of using new data as soon as it becomes available is the essence of the Gauss–Seidel iteration method, which is formulated as follows.

Gauss–Seidel Method

With respect to (A.1) and (A.2), assume $a_{ii} \neq 0$, $i = 1, 2, \cdots, n$. Define diagonal matrix D, lower triangular matrix E and upper triangular matrix F by

$$
D = \begin{pmatrix} a_{11} & & & O \\ & a_{22} & & \\ & & \ddots & \\ O & & & a_{nn} \end{pmatrix}, \quad
E = \begin{pmatrix} 0 & & & & O \\ a_{21} & 0 & & & \\ a_{31} & a_{32} & 0 & & \\ \vdots & \vdots & & \ddots & \\ a_{n1} & a_{n2} & \cdots & a_{n,n-1} & 0 \end{pmatrix},
$$

(A.9)

$$
F = \begin{pmatrix} 0 & a_{12} & a_{13} & \cdots & & a_{1n} \\ & 0 & a_{23} & \cdots & & a_{2n} \\ & & \ddots & & & \vdots \\ & & & & 0 & a_{n-1,n} \\ & O & & & & 0 \end{pmatrix}.
$$

Then

(A.10) $$A = D + E + F.$$

By (A.2) and (A.10)

$$(D + E)x = -Fx + b,$$

which, from the heuristic discussion above, suggests the iteration formula

(A.11) $$(D + E)x^{(k+1)} = -Fx^{(k)} + b, \quad k = 0, 1, 2, \cdots.$$

Finally, since D is nonsingular, so is $D + E$, so that (A.11) is equivalent to

(A.12) $$x^{(k+1)} = -(D + E)^{-1}Fx^{(k)} + (D + E)^{-1}b,$$

which is the Gauss–Seidel formula.

That the Gauss–Seidel formula actually does utilize new data as it arises follows readily from (A.11). For, (A.11) is the matrix form of the equations

(A.13)

$$a_{11}x_1^{(k+1)} = -a_{12}x_2^{(k)} - a_{13}x_3^{(k)} - a_{14}x_4^{(k)} - \cdots \qquad -a_{1n}x_n^{(k)} + b_1$$

$$a_{21}x_1^{(k+1)} + a_{22}x_2^{(k+1)} = -a_{23}x_3^{(k)} - a_{24}x_4^{(k)} - \cdots \qquad - a_{2n}x_n^{(k)} + b_2$$

$$a_{31}x_1^{(k+1)} + a_{32}x_2^{(k+1)} + a_{33}x_3^{(k+1)} = -a_{34}x_4^{(k)} - a_{35}x_5^{(k)} - \cdots - a_{3n}x_n^{(k)} + b_3$$

$$\cdot$$
$$\cdot$$
$$\cdot$$

$$a_{n1}x_1^{(k+1)} + a_{n2}x_2^{(k+1)} + \qquad \cdots \qquad + a_{nn}x_n^{(k+1)} = b_n.$$

However, since the $a_{ii} \neq 0$, $i = 1, 2, \cdots, n$, system (A.13) is equivalent to

(A.14)

$$x_1^{(k+1)} = -\frac{a_{12}}{a_{11}}x_2^{(k)} - \frac{a_{13}}{a_{11}}x_3^{(k)} - \cdots - \frac{a_{1n}}{a_{11}}x_n^{(k)} + \frac{b_1}{a_{11}}$$

$$x_2^{(k+1)} = -\frac{a_{21}}{a_{22}}x_2^{(k+1)} - \frac{a_{23}}{a_{22}}x_3^{(k)} - \frac{a_{24}}{a_{22}}x_4^{(k)} - \cdots - \frac{a_{2n}}{a_{22}}x_n^{(k)} + \frac{b_2}{a_{22}}$$

$$x_3^{(k+1)} = -\frac{a_{31}}{a_{33}}x_1^{(k+1)} - \frac{a_{32}}{a_{33}}x_2^{(k+1)} - \frac{a_{34}}{a_{33}}x_4^{(k)} - \cdots - \frac{a_{3n}}{a_{33}}x_n^{(k)} + \frac{b_3}{a_{33}}$$

$$\cdot$$
$$\cdot$$
$$\cdot$$

$$x_n^{(k+1)} = -\frac{a_{n1}}{a_{nn}}x_1^{(k+1)} - \frac{a_{n2}}{a_{nn}}x_2^{(k+1)} - \cdots - \frac{a_{n-1,n}}{a_{nn}}x_{n-1}^{(k+1)} + \frac{b_n}{a_{nn}}$$

and from (A.14) it is clear how new data is incorporated into the iteration as soon as it appears.

With regard to the Gauss–Seidel method, the following definitions are important.

Definition A.1

A permutation matrix is a square matrix whose elements are 0's and 1's and which satisfies the property that in each row and each column there exists exactly one 1.

Definition A.2

For $n \geq 2$, an $n \times n$ real matrix A is said to be reducible iff there exists an $n \times n$ permutation matrix P such that

$$(A.15) \qquad PAP^t = \begin{pmatrix} A_{1,1} & A_{1,2} \\ 0 & A_{2,2} \end{pmatrix},$$

where $A_{1,1}$ is an $r \times r$ submatrix, $A_{2,2}$ is an $(n - r) \times (n - r)$ submatrix, $1 \leq r < n$, and P^t is the transpose of matrix P.

Definition A.3

A real $n \times n$ matrix A, $n \geq 2$, is said to be **irreducible** if it is not reducible.

The matrix PAP^t in (A.15) is the result of interchanging various rows of A and corresponding columns. The significance of reducibility lies in the fact that for the linear algebraic system given by

$$PAP^t x = d$$

one could solve the final $(n - r)$ equations independently of the first r equations.

Definition A.4

For $n \geq 2$, a real $n \times n$ matrix $A = (a_{ij})$ is said to be properly diagonal dominant iff

$$(A.16) \qquad |a_{ii}| \geq \sum_{\substack{j=1 \\ j \neq i}}^{n} |a_{ij}|, \qquad i = 1, 2, \cdots, n,$$

and strict inequality is valid for at least one value of i.

Then the following important theorem is known (cf. Varga [1], p. 73).

Theorem A.1

For $n \geq 2$, let $A = (a_{ij})$ be a real, irreducible, properly diagonal dominant $n \times n$ matrix. Then, for any initial vector $x^{(0)}$, the Gauss–Seidel method converges to the solution of (A.2).

Motivated by Theorem A.1, an attempt can now be made to modify the Gauss–Seidel method in order to speed up the convergence. In this connection, consider (A.11), or, equivalently,

$$(A.17) \qquad Dx^{(k+1)} = Dx^{(k)} + [-Ex^{(k+1)} - (F + D)x^{(k)} + b].$$

Then (A.17) is a special case of the iteration formula

(A.18) $Dx^{(k+1)} = Dx^{(k)} + \omega[-Ex^{(k+1)} - (F + D)x^{(k)} + b]$,

where ω is a fixed, real constant. Reorganization of (A.18) yields

(A.19) $(D + \omega E)x^{(k+1)} = [-\omega F + (1 - \omega)D]x^{(k)} + \omega b$.

But if $a_{ii} \neq 0$, then D is nonsingular and so is $D + \omega E$ for any ω, so that (A.19) implies

(A.20) $x^{(k+1)} = (D + \omega E)^{-1}[-\omega F + (1 - \omega)D]x^{(k)} + (D + \omega E)^{-1}\omega b$.

Successive Over-relaxation

With respect to (A.1) and (A.2), assume $a_{ii} \neq 0$, $i = 1, 2, \cdots, n$. Define matrices D, E, F by (A.9). Then the successive over-relaxation iteration formula is (A.20).

In order to formulate a convergence theorem for the method of successive over-relaxation, the following definitions will be important.

Definition A.5

For $n \geq 2$, an $n \times n$ real matrix A is said to have "property A" iff there exists an $n \times n$ permutation matrix P such that

$$PAP^t = \begin{pmatrix} A_{1,1} & A_{1,2} \\ A_{2,1} & A_{2,2} \end{pmatrix}$$

where $A_{1,1}$ and $A_{2,2}$ are diagonal.

Definition A.6

For an $n \times n$ matrix A, the spectral norm of A, written $\sigma(A)$, is defined to be the absolute value of the maximum eigenvalue of A.

Definition A.7

Let T, S be $n \times n$ matrices and let b be an n-dimensional column vector. Let an iteration process $F(T,S,b)$ be defined by

$$x^{(n+1)} = Tx^{(n)} + Sb, \qquad n = 0, 1, 2, \cdots.$$

Then the rate of convergence $r(F)$ of the iteration process is defined by

$$r(F) = -\log \sigma(T).$$

(For the background that motivates Definition A.7, consult, for example, Varga [1] or Walker [1].)

The following theorem then is known (D. Young [1]).

Theorem A.2

For $n \geq 2$, let $A = (a_{ij})$ be a real, symmetric, positive definite matrix which possesses property A. If, with regard to (A.9) and Definition A.6, one lets

$$\mu = \sigma(D^{-1}[E + F])$$

then

$$0 \leq \mu < 1.$$

Furthermore, for any initial vector $x^{(0)}$ and any ω in the range $0 < \omega < 2$, it follows that the method of successive over-relaxation converges to the solution of (A.2) and that the value ω_b of ω which gives the maximum rate of convergence is given by

(A.21)
$$\omega_b = 1 + \left[\frac{\mu}{1 + \sqrt{1 - \mu^2}} \right]^2.$$

Concerning the numerical calculation of ω_b, consult Frankel [1], Garabedian [1], Parter [2], and D. Young [2]. For the extension of Theorem A.2 to nonsymmetric matrices consult Varga [1].

A.2. NONLINEAR SYSTEMS

Consider the system

(A.22)
$$f_i(x_1, x_2, \cdots, x_n) = 0, \qquad i = 1, 2, \cdots, n,$$

of n nonlinear equations in the n indicated unknowns. With regard to finding an approximate solution of elliptic boundary value problems, two iteration methods are of particular value, namely, Nonlinear Liebmann Iteration and the Generalized Newton's Method, each of which will be discussed next in turn.

Nonlinear Liebmann Iteration

If possible, solve the ith equation of (A.22) for the ith unknown, so that

$$x_1 = g_1(x_2, x_3, \cdots, x_n)$$
$$x_2 = g_2(x_1, x_3, \cdots, x_n)$$

(A.23)
$$\cdot$$
$$\cdot$$
$$\cdot$$
$$x_n = g_n(x_1, x_2, \cdots, x_{n-1}).$$

Then for any initial vector $x^{(0)}$ the method is defined by the iteration

$$x_1^{(k+1)} = g_1(x_2^{(k)}, x_3^{(k)}, \cdots, x_n^{(k)})$$
$$x_2^{(k+1)} = g_2(x_1^{(k+1)}, x_3^{(k)}, \cdots, x_n^{(k)})$$
(A.24)
$$x_3^{(k+1)} = g_3(x_1^{(k+1)}, x_2^{(k+1)}, x_4^{(k)}, \cdots, x_n^{(k)})$$

.
.
.

$$x_n^{(k+1)} = g_n(x_1^{(k+1)}, x_2^{(k+1)}, \cdots, x_{n-1}^{(k+1)})$$

for $k = 0, 1, 2, \cdots$.

Practical and theoretical aspects of Nonlinear Liebmann Iteration are explored in Bers [1], Greenspan and Yohe [1], and S. Schechter [2].

Generalized Newton's Method

With regard to (A.22), let $f_{ij} \equiv \dfrac{\partial f_i}{\partial x_j} \neq 0$. Then for ω a fixed, real constant, and for any initial vector $x^{(0)}$, the method is defined by the following iteration scheme:

$$x_1^{(k+1)} = x_1^{(k)} - \omega \frac{f_1(x_1^{(k)}, x_2^{(k)}, \cdots, x_n^{(k)})}{f_{11}(x_1^{(k)}, x_2^{(k)}, \cdots, x_n^{(k)})}$$

$$x_2^{(k+1)} = x_2^{(k)} - \omega \frac{f_2(x_1^{(k+1)}, x_2^{(k)}, \cdots, x_n^{(k)})}{f_{22}(x_1^{(k+1)}, x_2^{(k)}, \cdots, x_n^{(k)})}$$

(A.25)

. .   .
. .   .
. .   .

$$x_n^{(k+1)} = x_n^{(k)} - \omega \frac{f_n(x_1^{(k+1)}, x_2^{(k+1)}, \cdots, x_{n-1}^{(k+1)}, x_n^{(k)})}{f_{nn}(x_1^{(k+1)}, x_2^{(k+1)}, \cdots, x_{n-1}^{(k+1)}, x_n^{(k)})}$$

for $k = 0, 1, 2, \cdots$.

The Generalized Newton's Method is explored to some extent by Lieberstein [2] and Greenspan and Yohe [1]. It is of interest to note that if system (A.22) is linear and of form (A.2), then $f_{ii} \equiv a_{ii} \neq 0$, $i = 1, 2, \cdots, n$, and (A.25) reduces to successive over-relaxation. It is of further interest to note that no general mathematical theory has as yet been constructed for the Generalized Newton's Method.

BIBLIOGRAPHY

Ablow, C. M. and C. L. Perry

1. Iterative solutions of the Dirichlet problem for $\Delta u = u^2$. *Jour. Soc. Indust. Appl. Math.*, vol. 7, no. 4, 1959, 459–467.

2. Numerical solution of the Dirichlet problem for the quasilinear elliptic equation $\Delta u = buu$. *Abstracts of Short Communications*, I.C.M., Stockholm, 1962, 197.

Aizenstat, N. D.

1. On an estimate of the error in approximate solution of a finite-difference Poisson equation (Russian). *Mat. Sbornik N.S.*, 31(73), 1952, 485–490.

Akushsky, I.

1. On numerical solution of the Dirichlet problem on punched-card machines (Russian). *Bull. Acad. Sci. U.S.S.R.*, 54, 1946, 755–758.

Albrecht, R. F.

1. Approximation to the solution of partial differential equations by the solutions of ordinary differential equations. *Num. Mat.*, 2, 1960, 245–262.

Aleksidze, M.

1. On the numerical solution of the Dirichlet problem for Poisson equations (Russian). *Dokl. Akad. Nauk SSSR*, 147, 1962, 1271–1273.

Allen, D. N. de G. and S. C. R. Dennis

1. Graded nets in harmonic and biharmonic analysis. *Quart. Jour. Mech. Appl. Math.*, 4, 1951, 439–443.

2. The application of relaxation methods to the solution of differential equations in three dimensions, III. Three dimensional stress analysis. *Quart. Jour. Mech. Appl. Math.*, 11, 1958, 172–184.

Allen, D. N. de G. and B. Robins

1. The application of relaxation methods to satisfy normal-gradient boundary conditions associated with three dimensional partial differential equations. *Quart. Jour. Mech. Appl. Math.*, 15, 1962, 43–51.

Arms, R. J. and L. D. Gates, Jr.

1. The computation of an axially symmetric free boundary problem on NORC, part II. *U.S. Naval Proving Ground Report 1533*, Dahlgren, Va., 1957.

Badagadze, V. V.

1. Approximation of second order differential equations of elliptic type by difference equations (Russian). *Soobsc. Akad. Nauk Gruzin. SSSR*, 31, 1963, 263–269.

Bahvalov, N. S.

1. On a method for approximating solutions of Laplace's equation (Russian). *Dokl. Akad. Nauk SSSR*, (N.S.), 114, 1957, 455–458.

2. Numerical solution of the Dirichlet problem for Laplace's equation (Russian). *Vestnik Moskov. Univ. Ser. Mat. Meh. Astr. Fiz. Him.*, no. 5, 1959, 171–195.

Batschelet, E.

1. Uber die numerische Auflosung von Randwertproblemen bei elliptischen partiellen Differentialgleichungen. *ZAMP*, 3, 1952, 165–193.

Bellman, R., M. L. Juncosa, and R. Kalaba

1. Some numerical experiments using Newton's method for nonlinear parabolic and elliptic boundary-value problems. *Comm. A.C.M.*, 4, 1961, 187–191.

Berger, J. M. and G. J. Lasher

1. The use of discrete Green's functions in the numerical solution of Poisson's equation. *Ill. Jour. Math.*, vol. 2, no. 4A, 1958, 593–607.

Bergman, S.

1. A method for solving boundary value problems of mathematical physics on punch card machines. *Jour. Assoc. Comp. Mach.*, 1, 1954, 101–104.

2. Some methods for solutions of boundary-value problems of linear partial differential equations. *Proc. Symp. Appl. Math. AMS*, vol. 6, 1956, 11–29.

Bernstein, D. L.

1. *Existence theorems in partial differential equations.* Annals of Math. Studies, No. 23, Princeton University Press, Princeton, 1950.

Bernstein, F.

1. Neuer Galton Apparat zur Durchfuhrung einer praktischen Losung der Randwertaufgaben der partiellen Differentialgleichungen $\Delta u = 0$ und $\Delta u = C$ mit besonderer Berucksichtigung des Torsionproblems. *Zeits. f. Phys.*, 79, 1932, 684–695.

Bers, L.

1. On mildly nonlinear partial difference equations of elliptic type. *Jour. Res. Nat. Bur. Stand.*, vol. 51, no. 5, 1953, 229–236.

2. *Topology*. Lecture notes, New York University, 1956–1957.

Bickley, W. G.

1. Finite difference formulas for the square lattice. *Quart. Jour. Mech. Appl. Math.*, 1, 1948, 35–42.

Bickley, W. G., S. Michaelson, and M. R. Osborne

1. On finite-difference methods for the numerical solution of boundary-value problems. *Proc. Roy. Soc. London* A262, 1961, 219–236.

Birkhoff, G. and J. B. Diaz

1. Non-linear network problems. *Quart. Appl. Math.*, 13, 1956, 431–443.

Bramble, J. H. and B. E. Hubbard

1. On the formulation of finite difference analogues of the Dirichlet problem for Poisson's equation. *Num. Mat.*, 4, 1962, 313–327.

2. On a finite difference analogue of an elliptic boundary value problem which is neither diagonally dominant nor of non-negative type. *Jour. Math. Phys.*, XLIII, 1964, 117–132.

3. New monotone type approximations for elliptic problems. *Math. Comp.*, 18, 1964, 349–367.

Bramble, J. H. and L. E. Payne

1. Bounds for solutions of second order elliptic partial differential equations. Inst. Fluid Dyn. and Appl. Math., Tech. Note BN-237, College Park, Maryland, 1961.

Bruk, I. S.

1. A mechanical device for the approximate solution of the Poisson-Laplace equations (Russian). *Bull. Acad. Sci. U.S.S.R.*, 53, 1946, 311–312.

Burgerhout, T. J.

1. On the numerical solution of partial differential equations of elliptic type, I. *Appl. Sci. Res.*, B4, 1954, 161–172.

Cannon, J. R.

1. The numerical solution of the Dirichlet problem for Laplace's equation by linear programming. BNL 7129, Brookhaven Nat. Lab., Applied Math. Division.

Chow, T. S. and H. W. Milnes

1. Boundary contraction solution of Laplace's differential equation II. *Jour. Assoc. Comp. Mach.*, vol. 7, no. 1, 1960, 37–45.

2. Numerical solution of the Neumann and mixed boundary value problems by boundary contraction. *Jour. Assoc. Comp. Mach.*, vol. 8, no. 3, 1961, 336–358.

3. Solution of Laplace's equation by boundary contraction over regions of irregular shape. *Num. Mat.*, 4, 1962, 209–225.

Churchill, R. V.

1. *Fourier series and boundary value problems.* McGraw–Hill, New York, 1941.

Collatz, L.

1. Bemerkungen zur Fehlerabschatzung fur das Differenzenverfahren bei partiellen Differentialgleichungen. *ZAMM*, 13, 1933, 56–57.

2. *Numerical treatment of differential equations.* Springer, Berlin, 1960.

3. Monotonic operators in numerical mathematics. *Proc. Seventh Cong. Theor. Appl. Mech.*, Bombay, 1961, 253–258.

Conte, S. D. and R. T. Dames

1. An alternating direction method for solving the biharmonic equation. *MTAC*, 12, 1958, 198–205.

Cornock, A. F.

1. The numerical solution of Poisson's and the biharmonic equations by matrices. *Proc. Camb. Phil. Soc.*, 50, 1954, 524–535.

Courant, R.

1. *Dirichlet's principle, conformal mapping and minimal surfaces.* Interscience, New York, 1950.

Courant, R., K. Friedrichs, and H. Lewy

1. Uber die partiellen Differenzengleichungen der mathematischen Physik. *Math. Ann.*, 100, 1928, 32–74.

Courant, R. and D. Hilbert

1. *Methods of mathematical physics, II.* Interscience, New York, 1962.

Davidenko, D. F.

1. On the solution of Laplace's equation with axial symmetry by a difference method (Russian). *Dokl. Akad. Nauk SSSR*, 114, 1957, 690–693.

2. A difference method for the solution of the Poisson equation with axial symmetry (Russian). *Dokl. Akad. Nauk SSSR*, 118, 1958, 1066–1069.

3. Solution by the method of nets of the axi-symmetric Dirichlet problem for the Laplace equation (Russian). *Dokl. Akad. Nauk SSSR*, 126, 1959, 471–473.

4. Construction of difference equations for approximating the solution of the Euler-Poisson-Darboux equation (Russian). *Dokl. Akad. Nauk SSSR*, 142, 1962, 510–513.

Davidenko, D. F. and G. I. Biryuk
1. On the solution of Dirichlet's interval problem for Laplace's equation by the use of nets (Russian). *Dokl. Akad. Nauk SSSR*, 129, 1959, 246–249.

Davis, P. and P. Rabinowitz
1. Numerical experiments in potential theory using orthonormal functions. *Jour. Wash. Acad. Sciences*, 46, 1956, 12–17.

Diaz, J. B. and R. C. Roberts
1. Upper and lower bounds for the numerical solution of the Dirichlet difference boundary value problem. *Jour. Math. Phys.*, 31, 1952, 184–191.

2. On the numerical solution of the Dirichlet problem for Laplace's difference equation. *Quart. Appl. Math.*, 9, 1952, 355–360.

DiPasquale, S.
1. Generalization of the method of finite differences for the solution of equations with partial derivatives that can be reduced to a Laplace equation (Italian). *G. Gen. Civ.*, 97, 1959, 486–497.

Doob, J. L.
1. Discrete potential theory and boundaries. *Jour. Math. Mech.*, vol. 8, no. 3, 1959, 433–458.

Douglas, Jesse
1. Solution of the Plateau problem. *Trans. AMS*, 33, 1931, 264.

Douglas, Jim, Jr.
1. Alternating direction iteration for mildly nonlinear elliptic difference equations. *Num. Mat.*, 3, 1961, 92–108.

2. A correction to my paper "Alternating direction iteration for mildly nonlinear elliptic difference equations." *Num. Mat.*, 4, 1962, 301–302.

Downing, A. C., Jr.
1. On the convergence of steady state multiregion diffusion calculations. ORNL–2961, Oak Ridge National Laboratory, Oak Ridge, Tennessee, 1960.

Durand, E.
1. L'approximation du sixième ordre dans le calcul des solutions de l'équation de Poisson à trois variables. *C.R. Acad. Sci. Paris*, 245, 1957, 788–791.

2. Sur les solutions numériques de l'équation de Poisson. *Chiffres*, 1, 1958, 3–16.

Edwards, T. E.
1. Proton linear accelerator cavity calculations. MURA Rpt. 622, Off. Tech. Serv., U.S. Dept. Comm., 1961.

2. Messymesh (Program F-46). MURA Rpt. 642, Off. Tech. Serv., U.S. Dept. Comm., 1962.

Ehrlich, L. W.
1. Monte Carlo solutions of boundary value problems involving the difference analogue of $\dfrac{\partial^2 u}{\partial x^2} + \dfrac{\partial^2 u}{\partial y^2} + \dfrac{k}{y}\dfrac{\partial u}{\partial y} = 0$. *Jour. Assoc. Comp. Mach.*, vol. 6, no. 2, 1959, 204–218.

Ehrlich, L. W., J. D. Riley, W. G. Strang, and B. A. Troesch
1. Finite-difference techniques for a boundary problem with an eigenvalue in a boundary condition. *Jour. Soc. Industr. Appl. Math.*, vol. 9, no. 1, 1961, 149–164.

Eidus, D. M.
1. On the solution of boundary value problems by the difference method (Russian). *Dokl. Akad. Nauk SSSR*, (N.S.), 83, 1952, 191–194.
2. On the solution of boundary problems by the method of finite differences (Russian). *Dokl. Akad. Nauk SSSR*, 83, 1953, 191–194.

Eisemann, K.
1. Removal of ill-conditioning for matrices. *Quart. Appl. Math.*, 15, 1957, 225–230.

Emmons, H. W.
1. The numerical solution of partial differential equations. *Quart. Appl. Math.*, 2, 1944, 173–195.

Engeli, M. and P. Lauchli
1. Automatic calculation and programming of difference equations for elliptic boundary value problems. *Proc. IFIPS Cong.*, Munich, 1962.

Evans, D. J.
1. The solution of elliptic difference equations by stationary iterative processes. *Proc. Int. Conf. Inf. Proc.*, Information Processing, Unesco, Paris, 1960, 79–85.

Eve, J. and H. I. Scoins
1. A note on the approximate solution of the equations of Poisson and Laplace by finite difference methods. *Quart. Jour. Math. Oxford Ser.*, (2) 7, 1956, 217–223.

Fehlberg, E.
1. Bemerkungen zur numerischen Behandlung des Dirichletschen Problems fur spezielle Rander. *Acta Math.*, 87, 1952, 361–382.
2. Bemerkungen zur numerischen Behandlung des Dirichletschen Problems fur allgemeine Rander. *Acta Math.*, 91, 1954, 51–74.

Fichera, G.
1. Sull'approssimazione delle funzioni armoniche in tre variabili mediante successioni di particolari funzioni armoniche. *Rend. dell' Acc. Naz. Lincei*, 1947.

2. Formule di maggiorazione connesse ad una classe di transformazioni lineari. *Ann. Mat. Pura Appl.*, 36, 1954, 273–296.

3. Alcuni recenti sviluppi della teoria dei problemi al contorno per le equazioni alle derivate parziali lineari. Convegno Internazionale sulle Equazioni Lineari Alle Derivate Parziali, Trieste, 1954.

4. Su un principio di dualita per talune formule di maggiorazione relative alle equazioni differenziali. *Atti Accad. Naz. Lincei*, 19, 1955, 411–418.

Finn, R.
1. New estimates for equations of minimal surface type. *Arch. Rat. Mech. Anal.*, 14, 1963.

Forsythe, G. E.
1. Solving linear algebraic equations can be interesting. *Bull. AMS*, 59, 1953, 299–329.

2. Difference methods on a digital computer for Laplacian boundary value and eigenvalue problems. *Comm. Pure Appl. Math.*, 9, 1956, 425–434.

Forsythe, G. E. and T. S. Motzkin
1. An extension of Gauss' transformation for improving the condition of systems of linear equations. *MTAC*, 6, 1952, 9–17.

Forsythe, G. E. and W. Wasow
1. *Finite-difference methods for partial differential equations.* Wiley, New York, 1960.

Fox, L.
1. Solution by relaxation methods of plane potential problems with mixed boundary conditions. *Quart. Appl. Math.*, 2, 1944, 251–257.

2. The numerical solution of elliptic differential equations when the boundary conditions involve a derivative. *Phil. Trans. Roy. Soc. London*, [A], 242, 1950, 345–378.

3. *Numerical solution of ordinary and partial differential equations.* Addison-Wesley, Reading, Massachusetts, 1962.

Frank, P. and R. von Mises
1. *Die Differential- und Integralgleichungen der Mechanik und Physik*, I, Rosenberg, New York, 2nd ed., 1943.

Frankel, S.
1. Convergence rates of iterative treatments of partial differential equations. *MTAC*, 4, 1950, 65–75.

Franklin, J. N.
1. *Conservative matrices in the numerical solution of elliptic partial differential equations.* Lecture notes, California Institute of Technology, 1959.

Frey, T. and P. Rozsa

1. Konvergenzschnelle des Differenzverfahrens der Poissonschen und der biharmonischen Differentialgleichungen, I. *Period. Poly. Engrg.*, 4, 1960, 385–422.

Friedman, B.

1. The iterative solution of elliptic difference equations. Report NYO-7698. A.E.C. Computing Facility, New York University, 1957.

Friedrichs, K. O.

1. A finite difference scheme for the Neumann and the Dirichlet problem. Report NYO-9760, A.E.C. Computing Center, New York University, 1962,

Frocht, M. M.

1. The numerical solution of Laplace's equation in composite rectangular areas. *Jour. Appl. Phys.*, 17, 1946, 730–742.

Frocht, M. M. and M. M. Leven

1. A rational approach to the numerical solution of Laplace's equation. *Jour. Appl. Phys.*, 12, 1941, 596–604.

Gagua, M.

1. On approximate solution of linear boundary problems for elliptic equations (Russian). *Dokl. Akad. Nauk SSSR* (N.S.), 102, 1955, 1061–1064.

Garabedian, P. R.

1. Estimation of the relaxation factor for small mesh size. *MTAC*, 10, 1956, 183–185.

2. Applicazione al flurso supersonico del problema di Cauchy per un'equazione ellitica. *Atti Accad. Naz. Lincei Rend. Cl. Sci. Fis. Mat. Nat.*, (8) 24, 1958, 282–286.

Garza, A. de la

1. Error bounds for a numerical solution of a recurring linear system. *Quart. Appl. Math.*, 13, 1956, 453–456.

Geiringer, H.

1. On the solution of systems of linear algebraic equations by certain iteration methods. *Reissner Anniv. Volume*, Ann Arbor, Michigan, 1949, 365–393.

Gerschgorin, S.

1. On the approximate integration of the Laplace and Poisson differential equations (Russian). *Ann. Poly. Inst. Leningrad*, 30, 1927.

2. Fehlerabschatzung fur das Differenzenverfahren zur Lösung partieller Differentialgleichungen. *ZAMM*, 10, 1930, 373–382.

Giese, J. H.

1. On the truncation error in a numerical solution of the Neumann problem for a rectangle. *Jour. Math. Phys.*, vol. 37, no. 2, 1958, 169–177.

Giraud, G.

1. Sur certains problèmes non linéaires de Neumann et sur certains problèmes non linéaires mixtes. *Ann. Ec. N. Sup.*, 49, 1932, 1–104, 245–308.

2. Problèmes des types de Dirichlet et de Neumann dans certains cas où les données sont discontinués. *C. R. Ac. Sc. Paris*, 201, 1935, 925–928.

3. Nouvelle méthode pour traiter certains problèmes rélatifs aux équations du type elliptique. *Jour. de Math.*, 18, 1939, 111–143.

Goldstine, H. H. and J. von Neumann

1. Numerical inverting of matrices of high order, II. *Proc. AMS*, 2, 1951, 188–202.

Goodwin, E. T. (editor)

1. *Modern computing methods.* Philosophical Library, New York, 2nd ed., 1961.

Greenspan, D.

1. On evaluating the Stokes stream function by means of a symmetric difference analogue. *Riv. Mat. Univ. Parma*, 9, 1958, 87–93.

2. On a nine point method for the numerical evaluation of the Stokes stream function. *Port. Mat.*, 17, 1958, 97–106.

3. On the numerical solution of n-dimensional boundary value problems associated with Poisson's equation. *Jour. Frank. Inst.*, 266, 1958, 365–371.

4. Note on difference equation approximations of Laplace's equation. *Jour. Frank. Inst.*, 268, 1959, 46–52.

5. On the numerical solution of Dirichlet-type problems. *Amer. Math. Mo.*, 66, 1959, 40–46.

6. *Introduction to partial differential equations.* McGraw-Hill, New York, 1961.

7. On the approximate solution of a class of strongly elliptic linear differential equations. *Jour. Frank. Inst.*, 271, 1961, 471–487.

8. On the numerical solution of problems allowing mixed boundary conditions. *Jour. Frank. Inst.*, 277, 1964, 11–30.

9. Partial difference approximations with non-negative coefficients. *Jour. Frank. Inst.*, 275, 1963, 481–490.

10. The approximate solution of axially symmetric problems. *Comm. ACM*, 7, 1964, 373–377.

11. Recent computational results in the numerical solution of elliptic boundary value problems. Tech. Rpt. 408, Math. Res. Ctr., Madison, Wisconsin, 1963.

12. Numerical studies in approximating extremals of functionals. Tech. Rpt. 466, Math. Res. Ctr., Madison, Wisconsin, 1964.

Greenspan, D. and P. C. Jain
1. On non-negative difference analogues of elliptic differential equations. Tech. Rpt. 490, Math. Res. Ctr., Madison, Wisconsin, 1964.

Greenspan, D. and S. V. Parter
1. Mildly nonlinear elliptic partial differential equations and their numerical solution, II. Tech. Rpt. 474, Math. Res. Ctr., Madison, Wisconsin, 1964.

Greenspan, D. and R. Warten
1. On the approximate solution of Dirichlet-type problems with singularities on the boundary. *Jour. Frank. Inst.*, 273, 1962, 187–200.

Greenspan, D. and M. Yohe
1. On the approximate solution of $\Delta u = F(u)$. *Comm. ACM*, 6, 1963, 564–568.

Griffin, D. S. and R. S. Varga
1. Numerical solution of plane elasticity problems. *Jour. SIAM*, 11, 1963, 1046–1062.

Grunsch, H. J.
1. Eine Fehlerabschatzung bei der dritten Randwertaufgabe der Potential-theorie. *ZAMM*, 32, 1952, 279–281.

Hadamard, J. S.
1. *Lectures on Cauchy's problem in linear partial differential equations*. Dover, New York, 1952.

Hajdin, N.
1. Ein Verfahren zur numerischen Lösung der Randwertaufgaben vom elliptischen Typus. *Acad. Serbe Sci., Publ. Inst. Mat.*, 9, 1956, 69–78.

Hall, D. W. and G. L. Spencer, II
1. *Elementary topology*. Wiley, New York, 1955.

Hartee, D. R.
1. *Numerical analysis*. Clarendon Press, Oxford, England, 1952.

Heilbronn, H.
1. On discrete harmonic functions. *Proc. Camb. Phil. Soc.*, 45, 1949, 194–206.

Hestenes, M. R. and E. Stieffel
1. Method of conjugate gradients for solving linear systems. *Jour. Res. Nat. Bur. Stand.*, 49, 1952.

Hochstrasser, U. W.
1. Numerical experiments in potential theory using the Nehari estimates. *MTAC*, 12, 1958, 26–33.

Householder, A. S.
1. *Principles of numerical analysis*. McGraw-Hill, New York, 1953.

Huber, A.

1. On the uniqueness of generalized axially symmetric potentials. *Ann. Math.*, 60, 1954, 351–358.

2. Some results on generalized axially symmetric potentials. *Proc. Conf. Diff. Equations*, College Park, Maryland, 1955, 147–155.

Hyman, M. A.

1. Non-iterative numerical solution of boundary value problems. *Appl. Sci. Res.*, B2, 1952, 325–351.

2. On the numerical solution of partial differential equations. Thesis, Tech. Hogeschool, Delft, 1953.

Inoue, M.

1. Discrete Neumann problem. *Jour. Inst. Poly. Osaka City Univ.*, Ser. A5, 1954, 101–109.

Jackson, D.

1. *Fourier series and orthogonal polynomials.* Carus Monograph 6, Math. Assoc. Amer., 1941.

Jain, M. K.

1. Collocation method for physical problems. Thesis for the D.Sc., Indian Institute of Technology, Kharagpur, 1963.

John, F.

1. *Partial differential equations.* Lecture notes, New York University, 1952–1953.

2. *Advanced numerical analysis.* Lecture notes, New York University, 1956.

Kalaba, R.

1. On nonlinear differential equations, the maximum operation, and monotone convergence. *Jour. Math. Mech.*, 8, 1959, 519–574.

Kantorovich, L. and V. Krylov

1. *Approximate methods in higher analysis.* Noordhoff, Amsterdam, Netherlands, 1958.

Karlquist, O.

1. Numerical solution of elliptic difference equations by matrix methods. *Tellus*, 4, 1959, 374–384.

Keller, H. B.

1. Special block iterations with applications to Laplace and biharmonic difference equations. *SIAM Rev.*, 2, 1960, 277–287.

Kellogg, O. D.

1. *Foundations of potential theory.* Unger, New York, 1929.

Kelman, R. B.

1. Axisymmetrical potential problems suggested by biological considerations. *Bull. AMS*, 69, 1963, 835–838.

Klabukova, L. S.
1. Approximate method of solution for the problems of Hilbert and Poincaré (Russian). *Vycisl. Mat.*, 3, 1958, 34–87.

Kliot-Dasinskii, M. I.
1. On a method of solution of a plane problem in potential theory (Russian). *Leningrad Inzen.-Stroit. Inst. Sb. Nauk Trudov*, 17, 1954, 11–27.

Korolyuk, V. S.
1. On a method of increasing the asymptotic accuracy of the method of grids (Russian). *Dokl. Akad. Nauk SSSR*, (N.S.) 101, 1955, 985–987.

Krylov, N. and N. Bogoliubov
1. Application de la méthode de l'algorithme variationnel à la solution approchée des équations différentielles aux derivées partielles du type elliptique, I, II. *Bull. Acad. Sci. Leningrad*, 1930, 43–71, 105–114.

Kunin, I. A.
1. Approximate method of solution of boundary value problems for certain equations of elliptic type (Russian). *Izv. Akad. Nauk SSSR, Otd. Tekh. Nauk*, no. 10, 1958, 146–149.

Kunz, K. S.
1. *Numerical analysis*. McGraw-Hill, New York, 1957.

Laasonen, P.
1. On the degree of convergence of discrete approximations for the solutions of the Dirichlet problem. *Ann. Acad. Sci. Fenn. A. I.*, 246, 1957, 1–19.
2. On the truncation error of discrete approximations to the solutions of Dirichlet problems in a domain with corners. *Jour. Assoc. Comp. Mach.*, vol. 5, no. 1, 1958, 32–38.
3. On the solution of Poisson's difference equation. *Jour. Assoc. Comp. Mach.*, 5, 1958, 370–382.

Ladyzenskaya, O. A.
1. The method of finite differences in the theory of partial differential equations. *AMS Translations*, series 2, vol. 20, 1962, 77–104.

Landau, H. G.
1. A simple procedure for improved accuracy in the resistor-network solution of Laplace's and Poisson's equations. *Jour. Appl. Mech.*, March, 1957, 93–97.

Langer, R. E. (editor)
1. *Partial differential equations and continuum mechanics*. Univ. Wisconsin Press, Madison, Wisconsin, 1961.

Lax, P.
1. *Partial differential equations*. Lecture notes, New York University, 1950–1951.

Lebedev, V. I.

1. Dirichlet's and Neumann's problems on triangular and hexagonal lattices. *Soviet Math.*, 2, 1961, 519–522.

2. Four-point schemes of increased accuracy (Russian). *Dokl. Akad. Nauk SSSR*, 142, 1962, 526–529.

Le Roux, J.

1. Sur le problème de Dirichlet. *Jour. Math.*, 10, 1914, 189–230.

Lesky, P.

1. Calcolo numerico: Ricerca di una funzione armonica soggetta a condizioni al contorno non lineari. *Rend. Accad. Sci. Fis. Mat. Napoli*, (4) 19, 1953, 145–149.

Levinson, N.

1. Dirichlet problem for $\Delta u = f(P,u)$. *Jour. Math. Mech.*, 12, 1963, 567–576.

Lichtenstein, L.

1. Randwertaufgaben der Theorie der linearen partiellen Differentialgleichungen zweiter Ordnung vom elliptischen Typus, II. *Jour. fur Math.*, 143, 1913, 51–105.

2. Neuere Entwicklung der Theorie partial Differentialgleichungen zweiter Ordnung vom elliptischen Typus. *Enzyklopadie der mathematischen Wissenschaften*, 2, part 3, Teubner, Leipzig, 1923–1927, 1303–1305.

Lieberstein, H. M.

1. A numerical test case for the nonlinear overrelaxation algorithm. Tech. Rpt. 122, Math. Res. Ctr., Madison, Wisconsin, 1960.

2. A continuous method in numerical analysis applied to examples from a new class of boundary value problems. Tech. Rpt. 175, Math. Res. Ctr., Madison, Wisconsin, 1960.

Liebmann, H.

1. Die angenahrte Ermittling harmonischer Funktionen und konformer Abbildungen. *Sitz-Ber. boyr. Akad. Wiss. Munchen*, math.-phys. Klasse, 1918, 385–416.

Littman, W.

1. Finite difference methods for elliptic equations of arbitrary order. *Notices of AMS*, Abstract 546–67, 1958.

Lyusternik, L. A.

1. On general network approximations of the Laplace operator (Russian). *Dokl. Akad. Nauk SSSR* (N.S.), 91, 1953, 1267–1269.

2. On difference approximations of the Laplace operator (Russian). *Uspehi Mat. Nauk* (N.S.), 9, no. 2 (60), 1954, 3–66.

3. A difference analogue of Green's function in three space (Russian). *Vycislit Mat.*, 1, 1957, 3–22.

MacNeal, R. H.

1. An asymmetrical finite difference network. *Quart. Appl. Math.*, 11, 295–310.

Maiorov, I. V.

1. Approximate solutions of equations of elliptic type (Russian). *Izv. Vyss. Ucebn. Zaved. Mat.*, no. 3 (4), 1958, 160–162.

Mangasarian, O. L.

1. Numerical solution of the first biharmonic problem by linear programming. *Int. Jour. Eng. Sci.*, 1, 1963, 231–240.

Mendelsohn, N. S.

1. Some elementary properties of ill conditioned matrices and linear equations *Amer. Math. Mo.*, 63, 1956, 285–294.

Mikeladze, S. E.

1. On the numerical solution of the equations of Laplace and Poisson (Russian). *Izv. Akad. Nauk SSSR, Ser. Math.*, no. 2, 1938, 271–290.

2. On the integration of differential equations by the difference method (Russian). *Izv. Akad. Nauk SSSR, Ser. Math.*, 1939, 627–642.

3. On the question of numerical integration of partial differential equations by means of nets (Russian). *Mitt. Georg. Abt. Akad. Wiss. USSR*, 1, 1940, 249–254.

4. On the solution of boundary value problems by the difference method (Russian). *C. R. (Doklady) Acad. Sci. USSR*, (N.S.) 28, 1940, 400–402.

5. Numerical integration of equations of elliptic and parabolic type (Russian). *Izv. Akad. Nauk SSSR*, 5, 1941, 57–74.

Milne, W. E.

1. *Numerical calculus.* Princeton Univ. Press, Princeton, 1950.

2. Numerical methods associated with Laplace's equation. *Proceedings of the Second Symposium on Large Scale Digital Calculating Machines*, Harvard Univ. Press, Cambridge, Massachusetts, 1951, 152–163.

3. *Numerical solution of differential equations.* Wiley, New York, 1953.

Milnes, H. W. and R. B. Potts

1. Numerical solution of partial differential equations by boundary contraction. *Quart. Appl. Math.*, vol. 18, no. 1, 1960, 1–13.

Miranda, C.

1. Approssimazione di una funzione armonica in tre variabili mediante polinomii armonici. *Rend. Circ. Mat. Palermo*, 1932.

2. Sull'approssimazione delle funzioni armoniche in tre variabili. *Rend. Acc. Naz. Lincei*, 1948.

3. *Equazioni alle derivate parziali di tipo ellitico.* Springer, Berlin, 1955.

Miyakoda, K.

1. Numerical calculations of Laplacian and Jacobian using 9 and 25 gridpoint systems. *Jour. Meteorol. Soc. Japan* (II), 38, 1960, 94–106.

2. Test of convergence speed of iterative methods for solving 2- and 3-dimensional elliptic-type differential equations. *Jour. Meteorol. Soc. Japan*, (II) 38, 1960, 107–124.

Moskovitz, D.

1. The numerical solution of Laplace's and Poisson's equations. *Quart. Appl. Math.*, 2, 1944, 148–163.

Motzkin, T. S. and W. Wasow

1. On the approximation of linear elliptic partial differential equations with positive coefficients. *Jour. Math. Phys.*, 31, 1953, 253–259.

Muller, M. E.

1. On discrete operators connected with the Dirichlet problem. *Jour. Math. Phys.*, 35, 1956, 89–113.

Myerott, R. E., P. J. Luke, W. W. Clendenin, and S. Geltman

1. A numerical variational method. *Phys. Review*, II., series 85, 1952, 393–400.

Mysovskih, I. P.

1. Application of Caplygin's method to the solution of the Dirichlet problem for a special type of elliptic differential equation (Russian). *Dokl. Akad. Nauk SSSR* (N.S.), 99, 1954, 13–15.

2. On a boundary problem for the equation $\Delta u = k(x,y)u^2$ (Russian). *DAN*, 94, 1954, 995–998.

Nehari, Z.

1. *Conformal mapping*. McGraw-Hill, New York, 1952.

2. On the numerical solution of the Dirichlet problem. *Proc. Conf. Diff. Equations*, College Park, Maryland, 1956, 157–178.

Newman, D. J.

1. *Numerical solution of a Cauchy problem for elliptic partial differential equations*. AVCO Manuf. Corp, Lawrence, Massachusetts, 1957.

Nirenberg, L.

1. Existence theorems in partial differential equations. Unpublished lecture notes, New York University.

2. On elliptic partial differential equations. *Ann. Scuola Norm. Sup. Pisa*, series III, vol. 13, 1959, 1–48.

Nitsche, J. and J. C. C. Nitsche

1. Error estimates for the numerical solution of elliptic differential equations. *Arch. Rat. Mech. and Anal.*, 5, 1960, 293–306.

Nitsche, J. C. C. and J. Nitsche
1. Fehlerabschatzung fur die numerische Berechnung von Integralen, die Lösungen elliptischer Differentialgleichungen enthalten. *Arch. Rat. Mech. Anal.*, vol. 5, no. 4, 1960, 307–314.

O'Brien, G. G., M. A. Hyman, and S. Kaplan
1. A study of the numerical solution of partial differential equations. *Jour. Math. Phys.*, 29, 1951, 223–251.

Panov, D. J.
1. An approximate graphical solution of the boundary problems of Laplace's equation (Russian). *Trans. Center Aero-Hydro. Inst.*, nr. 169, 1934, 3–24.
2. The numerical solution of boundary value problems of partial differential equations of elliptic type (Russian). *Uspekhi Matem. Nauk*, 4, 1938, 34–44.

Parter, S. V.
1. Some computational results on "two-line" iterative methods for the biharmonic difference equation. *Jour. Assoc. Comp. Mach.*, 8, 1961, 359–365.
2. On estimating the "rates of convergence" of iterative methods for elliptic difference equations. Tech. Rpt. 28, Appl. Math. and Stat. Labs., Stanford Univ., Palo Alto, California, 1963.
3. Mildly nonlinear elliptic partial differential equations and their numerical solution, I. Tech. Rpt. 470, Math. Res. Ctr., Madison, Wisconsin, 1964.

Payne, L. E. and H. F. Weinberger
1. New bounds in harmonic and biharmonic problems. *Jour. Math. Phys.*, vol. 33, no. 4, 1955, 291–307.

Peaceman, D. W. and H. H. Rachford, Jr.
1. The numerical solution of parabolic and elliptic differential equations. *Jour. Soc. Ind. Appl. Math.*, 3, 1955, 28–41.

Perron, O.
1. Eine neue Behandlung der Randwertaufgabe fur $\Delta u = 0$. *Math. Z.*, 18, 1923, 42–54.

Petrovsky, I. G.
1. New proof of the existence of a solution of Dirichlet's problem by the method of finite differences (Russian). *Uspekhi Matem. Nauk*, 18, 1941, 161–170.
2. *Lectures on partial differential equations.* Interscience, New York, 1957.

Phillips, H. and N. Wiener
1. Nets and the Dirichlet problem. *Jour. Math. Phys.*, 2, 1923, 105–124.

Picard, E.
1. Mémoire sur la théorie des équations aux dérivées partielles et la méthode des approximations successives. *Jour. Math. Pures et Appl.*, series 4, tome vi, 1890, 145–210.

Picone, M.

1. Nuovo metodo d'approssimazione per la soluzione del problema di Dirichlet. *Reale Acc. Naz. Lincei*, 31, 1922, 357–359.

2. Sul metodo delle minime potenze ponderate e sul metodo di Ritz per il calcolo approssimato nei problemi della fisica matimatica. *Rend. Circ. Mat. Palermo*, 1928.

Pohozaev, S. T.

1. The Dirichlet problem for the equation $\Delta u = u^2$. *Soviet Math.*, 1960, 1143–1146.

Polozii, G. N.

1. A numerical method of solving boundary value problems for partial differential equations. *Soviet Math.*, 1, 1960, 1016–1019.

Pucci, C.

1. Sui problemi di Cauchy non "ben posti". *Rend. Acc. Naz. Lincei*, XVIII, 1955, 473–478.

Rado, T.

1. *On the problem of Plateau.* Chelsea, New York, 1951.

Richardson, L. F.

1. The approximate arithmetical solution by finite differences of physical problems involving differential equations with an application to the stresses in a masonry dam. *Phil. Trans. Roy. Soc. London*, 210A, 1910, 307–357.

Richardson, R. G. D.

1. A new method in boundary problems for differential equations. *Trans. AMS*, 18, 1917, 489–518.

Riley, J. D.

1. Iteration procedures for the Dirichlet difference problem. *MTAC*, 1954, 125–131.

Rosenbloom, P. C.

1. On the difference equation method for solving the Dirichlet problem. *NBS AMS*, 18, 1952, 231–237.

Rosser, J. B.

1. Block relaxation by computer. Tech. Rpt. 477, Math. Res. Ctr., Madison, Wisconsin, 1964.

Roudebush, W. H.

1. Analysis of discretization errors for differential equations with discontinuous coefficients. Ph.D. thesis. Case Institute of Technology, 1963.

Rowe, P. P.

1. Difference approximations to partial derivatives for uneven spacings in the network. *Trans. Amer. Geophys. Union*, 36, 1955, 995–1008.

Runge, C.

1. Uber eine Methode die partielle Differentialgleichung $\Delta u = $ constans numerisch zu integrieren. *Zeits. f. Math. u. Phys.*, 56, 1908–1909, 225–232.

2. Graphische Losung von Randwertaufgaben der Gleichung $\nabla^2 u = 0$. *Nach. Gott. Math. Phys. Klasse*, 1911, 431–448.

Saltzer, C.

1. Discrete potential and boundary value problems. Tech. Rpt. 371, Math. Res. Ctr., Madison, Wisconsin, 1962.

Saulev, V. K.

1. An example of an application of S. L. Sobolev's imbedding theorem to numerical mathematics (Russian). *Dokl. Akad. Nauk SSSR*, 147, 1962, 303–305.

Schechter, M.

1. On the Dirichlet problem for second order elliptic equations with coefficients singular at the boundary. *Comm. Pure Appl. Math.*, 13, 1960, 321–328.

Schechter, S.

1. Relaxation methods for linear equations. *Comm. Pure Appl. Math.*, 12, 1959, 313–335.

2. Iteration methods for nonlinear problems. *Trans. AMS*, 1962, 179–189.

Schneider, E.

1. Uber eine neue Methode zur angenaherten numerischen Integration der Laplaceschen Differentialgleichungen, zugleich ein Beitrag zur Theorie der Torsion. *Diss. Jena*, Weida i. Thur.: Thomas u Hubert, 50 S. 8°, 1916.

Schot, J. W.

1. On the numerical solution of Poisson's equation in an elliptic region. Interim Tech. Rpt. 29, Dept. of Army project 5B99-01-004, Dept. of Math., University of Maryland, 1957.

Schroder, J.

1. Zur Losung von Potentialaufgaben mit Hilfe des Differenzenverfahrens. *ZAMM*, 34, 1954, 241–253.

Sheldon, J. W.

1. On the numerical solution of elliptic difference equations. *MTAC*, 1955, 101–112.

2. Algebraic approximations for Laplace's equation in the neighborhood of interfaces. *MTAC*, 12, 1958, 174–186.

Sheldon, J. W. and D. P. Squier

1. Remarks on the order of convergence of discrete analogs for second-order elliptic partial differential equations. *SIAM Rev.*, vol. 4, no. 4, 1962, 366–378.

Shortley, G. H. and R. Weller

1. The numerical solution of Laplace's equation. *Jour. Appl. Phys.*, 9, 1938, 334–348.

Shortley, G. H., R. Weller, P. Darbey, and E. H. Gamble

1. Numerical solution of axisymmetrical problems, with applications to electrostatics and torsion. *Eng. Exp. Sta. Bull. No. 128*, Ohio State University, 1947.

Shortley, G. H., R. Weller, and B. Fried

1. Numerical solution of Laplace's and Poisson's equations. *Eng. Exp. Sta. Bull. No. 107*, Ohio State University, 1940.

Shuleshko, P.

1. A method of integration over the boundary for solving boundary value problems. *Austral. Jour. Appl. Sci.*, 12, 1961, 393–406.

Slobodyanskii, M. G.

1. Approximate solution of some boundary problems for elliptic differential equations and estimates of the error (Russian). *Dokl. Akad. Nauk SSSR* (N.S.), 89, 1953, 221–224.

2. Method of approximate integration of differential equations with partial derivatives and its application to problems of elasticity. (Russian) *Appl. Math. Mech., Moscow*, (2)3, no. 1, 75–82.

Sneddon, I. N.

1. *Elements of partial differential equations.* McGraw-Hill, New York, 1957.

Sobrero, L.

1. Un metodo di approssimazioni successive per la risoluzione del problema di Dirichlet. *Ann. Scuola Norm. Super. Pisa* (3), 3, 1949, 1950, 67–93.

Southwell, R. V.

1. *Relaxation methods in engineering science.* Oxford Univ. Press, Oxford, England, 1940.

Southwell, R. V. and G. Vaisey

1. Plane potential problems involving specified normal gradients. *Proc. Roy. Soc. London*, A182, 1943, 129–151.

Squier, D. P.

1. On the existence and uniqueness of solutions of the Poisson interface problem. *Amer. Jour. Math.*, 85, 1963, 241–247.

Stein, P. and J. E. L. Peck

1. On the numerical solution of Poisson's equation over a rectangle. *Pac. Jour. Math.*, 5, Suppl. II, 1955, 999–1011.

Sternberg, W.
1. Die Theorie der Randwertaufgaben im Gebiete der partiellen Differential-gleichungen. *Pascal's Repertorium der hoheren Mathematic*, 1, part 3, Teubner, Leipzig, 1929, 1121–1139.

Sternberg, W. and T. I. Smith
1. *The theory of potential and spherical harmonics.* Univ. Toronto Press, Toronto, Canada, 1946.

Stiefel, E.
1. La machina à calculer arithmétique "Z4" de l'École Polytechnique Federale a Zurich (Suisse) et son application à la resolution d'une équation aux dérivées partielles de type elliptique. *Centre Nat. Rech. Sci., Paris*, colloq. no. 37, 1953.

Strang, W. G.
1. Difference methods for mixed boundary-value problems. *Duke Math. Jour.*, 27, 1960, 221–232.

Stresneva, V. A.
1. Auxiliary tables for the solution of Poisson's equation for polygonal regions by the method of reduction to ordinary differential equations (Russian). *Trudy Mat. Inst. Steklov*, 53, 1959, 267–282.

Sugai, I.
1. Numerical solution of Laplace's equation given Cauchy conditions. *I. B. M. Jour. Res. Dev.*, 3, 1959, 187–188.

Sunatani, C. and S. Negoro
1. On a method of approximate solution of a plane harmonic function. *Trans. Soc. Mech. Eng., Tokyo*, 3, 1937, 6–11.

Synge, J. L.
1. *The hypercircle in mathematical physics.* Cambridge Univ. Press, Cambridge, England, 1957.

Thomeé, V.
1. Elliptic difference operators and Dirichlet's problem. Tech. note BN-345, Inst. Fluid Dyn. Appl. Math, College Park, Maryland, 1964.

Titchmarsh, E. C.
1. *The theory of functions.* Oxford Univ. Press, Oxford, England, 1939.

Todd. J.
1. Experiments in the solution of differential equations by Monte Carlo methods. *Jour. Wash. Acad. Sci.*, vol. 44, no. 12, 1954, 377–381.

Todd, J. (editor)
1. *Survey of numerical methods.* McGraw-Hill, New York, 1962.

Tranter, C. J.

1. The combined use of relaxation methods and Fourier transforms in the solutions of some three-dimensional boundary value problems. *Quart. Jour. Mech. Appl. Math.*, 1, 1948, 281–286.

Trytten, G. N.

1. Pointwise bounds for solutions of the Cauchy problem for elliptic equations. NOL TR 62-91, Naval Ord. Lab., White Oak, Maryland, 1962.

Uhlmann, W.

1. Differenzenverfahren fur die 2 and 3 Randwertaufgabe mit krummlinigen Randern bei $\Delta u(x,y) = r(x,y,u)$. *ZAMM*, 38, 1958, 226–251.

2. Uber harmonische und isotrope stochastische Prozesse mit Fehlerschatzung fur ein Differenzenverfahren. *ZAMM*, 41, 1961, 428–447.

3. Uber den Fehler bei Differenzenverfahren fur die Poissonsche Differential-gleichung. *Num. Mat.*, 4, 1962, 226–237.

Varga, R. S.

1. *Matrix iterative analysis.* Prentice-Hall, Englewood Cliffs, New Jersey, 1962.

Vekua, I. N.

1. A boundary problem with oblique derivative for an equation of elliptic type (Russian). *Dokl. Akad. Nauk SSSR* (N.S.), 92, 1953, 1113–1116.

Visik, M. I. and O. A. Ladyzenskaya

1. Boundary value problems for partial differential equations and certain classes of operator equations. *AMS Translations*, series 2, vol. 10, 223–282.

Viswanathan, R. V.

1. Solution of Poisson's equation by relaxation method: normal gradient specified on curved boundaries. *MTAC*, 11, 1957, 67–78.

Vlasov, V. K. and A. B. Bakusinskii

1. The method of potentials and the numerical solution of the Dirichlet problem for the Laplace equation (Russian). *Z. Vycisl. Mat. i Mat. Fiz.*, 3, 1963, 574–580.

Vlasova, Z. A.

1. A numerical realization of the method of reduction to ordinary differential equations (Russian). *Sibirsk. Mat. Z.*, 4, 1963, 475–479.

Volkov, E. A.

1. On a solution by the method of grids of equations of elliptic type with boundary conditions containing derivatives (Russian). *Dokl. Akad. Nauk SSSR* (N.S.), 102, 1955, 437–440.

2. On the solution by the method of nets of the interior Dirichlet problem for the Laplace equation (Russian). *Vycisl. Mat.*, 1, 1957, 34–61.

3. Investigation of a method for increasing the accuracy of the net method for the solution of Poisson's equation (Russian). *Vycisl. Mat.*, 1, 1957, 62–80.

Vzorova, A. I.

1. *Tables for the solution of Laplace's equation on an elliptic region* (Russian). Academy of Science, Moscow, 1957.

Wachspress, E. L.

1. The numerical solution of boundary value problems. *Mathematical Methods for Digital Computers*, Wiley, New York, 1960, 121–127.

Walker, M. S.

1. Iterative methods for the solution of elliptic partial differential equations. Associateship thesis, Royal College of Science and Technology, Glasgow, 1961.

Walsh, J. L.

1. Solution of the Dirichlet problem for the ellipse by interpolating harmonic polynomials. *Jour. Math. Mech.*, 9, 1960, 193–196.

Walsh, J. L. and D. Young

1. On the accuracy of the numerical solution of the Dirichlet problem by finite differences. *Jour. Res. Nat. Bur. Stand.*, vol. 51, no. 6, 1953, 343–363.

2. On the degree of convergence of solutions of difference equations to the solution of the Dirichlet problem. *Jour. Math. Phys.*, 33, 1954, 80–93.

3. Lipschitz conditions for harmonic and discrete harmonic functions. *Jour. Math. Phys.*, vol. 36, no. 2, 1957, 138–150.

Warschawski, S. E.

1. Recent results in numerical methods of conformal mapping. *Proc. Symp. Appl. Math.*, AMS, vol. 6, 1956.

Warten, R. M.

1. On the approximate solution of axially symmetric problems by means of finite differences. Ph.D. thesis, Purdue University, August, 1961.

Wasow, W.

1. Random walks and the eigenvalues of elliptic difference equations. *Jour. Res. Nat. Bur. Stand.*, vol. 46, no. 1, 1951, 65–73.

2. On the truncation error in the solution of Laplace's equation by finite differences. *Jour. Res. Nat. Bur. Stand.*, 48, 1952, 345–348.

3. Discrete approximations to elliptic differential equations. *ZAMP*, 6, 1955, 81–97.

4. The accuracy of difference approximations to plane Dirichlet problems with piecewise analytic boundary values. *Quart. Appl. Math.*, 15, 1957, 53–63.

Weinberger, H. F.

1. Upper and lower bounds for eigenvalues by finite difference methods. *Comm. Pure Appl. Math.*, 9, 1956, 613–623.

2. Exact information by finite difference approximation. Tech. Note BN-173, Inst. Fluid Dynamics and Applied Math., College Park, Maryland, 1959.

Weinstein, A.

1. Generalized axially symmetric potential theory. *Bull. AMS*, 59, 1953, 20–38.

2. Singular partial differential equations and their applications. *Proc. Symp. Fluid Dyn. and Appl. Math. at Univ. Md.*, 1961; Gordon and Breach, New York, 1963, 29–49.

Weller, R., G. H. Shortly, and B. Fried

1. Solution of torsion problems by numerical integration of Poisson's equation. *Jour. Appl. Phys.*, 11, 283–290.

Whitehead, S.

1. An approximate solution for the distribution of temperature or potential with cylindrical isothermal or equipotential surfaces. *Proc. Phys. Soc. Lond.*, 54, 63–65.

Wilson, W. L.

1. On discrete Dirichlet and Plateau problems. *Num. Mat.*, 3, 1961, 359–373.

Wise, H. and C. M. Ablow

1. Diffusion and heterogeneous reaction, IV. *Jour. Chem. Phys.*, 35, 1961, 10–18.

Wolf, F.

1. Uber die angenaherte numerische Berechnung harmonischer und biharmonischer Funktionen. *ZAMM*, 6, 1926, 118–150.

Woods, L. C.

1. The relaxation treatment of singular points in Poisson's equation. *Quart. Jour. Mech. Appl. Math.*, 6, 1953, 163–185.

Young, D.

1. Iterative methods for solving partial difference equations of elliptic type. *Trans. AMS*, 76, 1954, 92–111.

2. ORDVAC solutions of the Dirichlet problem. *Jour. Assoc. Computing Machinery*, 2, 1955, 137–161.

3. The numerical solution of elliptic and parabolic partial differential equations. *Survey of Numerical Analysis*, McGraw-Hill, New York, 1962, pp 380–438.

Young, D. and H. Shaw

1. ORDVAC solutions of $\dfrac{\partial^2 y}{\partial x^2} + \dfrac{\partial^2 u}{\partial y^2} + \dfrac{k}{y}\dfrac{\partial u}{\partial y} = 0$ for boundary value problems and problems of mixed type. Interim Tech. Rpt. No. 14, U.S. Army Contract DA-36-034-ORD-1486. Mathematics Dept., Univ. Maryland, College Park, Maryland, 1955.

Young, D. and C. H. Warlick
1. On the use of Richardson's method for the numerical solution of Laplace's equation on the ORDVAC. Ballistic Res. Labs. Rpt. 707, Aberdeen Proving Grounds, Maryland, 1953.

Young, J. D.
1. Application of linear programming to the solution of linear differential equations. Univ. Cal., Lawrence Rad. Lab., Berkeley, Cal., UCRL-10110, March 1, 1962.

Zaremba, S.
1. Sur le calcul numérique des fonctions demandées dans le problème de Dirichlet et le problème hydrodynamique. International de l'Académie des Science de Cracovie, *Bulletin*, 1909, 125–195.

INDEX